HALLEY'S COMET

A MYSTERIOUS VISITOR
FROM OUTER SPACE

HALLEY'S COMET

A Mysterious Visitor
from Outer Space

Terence Dickinson

Edmund Scientific
Barrington, N.J.

Library of Congress catalog card number: 84-073498
Printed in the United States of America

Contents

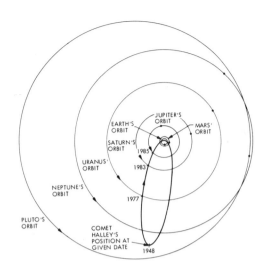

ACKNOWLEDGMENTS

*The author greatly appreciates
the helpful comments of David Levy
and the excellent information and advice
proviced by Donald Yeomans. Susan Dickinson's
tireless work in preparing the final
manuscript made this
book happen.*

1
The Comet Is Coming

Halley's Comet is coming. Hurtling at 20 times the speed of a Concorde jetliner, this most famous of all comets is closing in on one of its once-in-a-lifetime swings past the Earth.

In January 1985 the comet crossed Jupiter's orbit, 500 million miles from the sun. During the summer it traverses the asteroid belt on its headlong plunge toward the solar system's heart. By November amateur astronomers will be scanning for the cosmic tourist with backyard telescopes. Almost every telescope on Earth, from spotting scopes to the giant at Mount Palomar, will be pointed at the mysterious visitor from the abyss during its furious swing by the sun in the winter of 1985-86.

Despite its fame, Halley's Comet is thought to be nothing more than a flying mountain of ice about two miles across. But like fireflies at night, comets such as

Halley, when stimulated, can put on a show far out of proportion to their actual size.

Comets spend almost all their lives in the celestial deep-freeze of the outer solar system. Halley, for example, was beyond the orbit of Uranus from the end of the First World War until 1978. But when a comet nears the sun, solar radiation vaporizes the icy surface, splashing a wondrous diaphanous tail across the blackness of space. That's what caused all the commotion during Halley's last visit in 1910. Historical records tell us that the striking visitor has decorated the sky at 76-year intervals dating back to at least 240 B.C.

This time around, Halley will be greeted by five spacecraft sent from Earth to view the spectacle close up. At least one will plummet through the densest parts of the comet's tail. Slashing of the U.S. space budget in recent years eliminated an American ship from the armada. U.S. scientists will be watching from Earth. And that's too bad, because Halley's Comet will not venture as close to Earth as it did back in 1910. Early in January 1986, and again in March and April, it should be visible to the unaided eye—but barely. We will get to the reasons for that later.

Mark Twain once called comets "unaccountable freaks." These ghostly objects, with tails that are far more tenuous than mist, can come uncomfortably close to Earth. Many have swooped to within a few million miles. Only the moon and a handful of asteroids are known to ever approach closer. Yet compared to these other objects, comets remain shrouded in mystery. Most of them appear unexpectedly, seemingly materializing from nowhere, as if to provide sport for amateur astronomers who spend countless evenings seeking them.

A comet's headlong plunge toward the sun can be suicidal because our star's radiation rapidly boils gases from its icy body, sweeping the vapors back into a filmy tail. At least one comet is known to have plunged right into the sun. A typical comet makes a hairpin turn around the sun, emerging with a longer and brighter tail than it had when it went in. It punctuates the sky like an exclamation mark for a few weeks, then retreats tail first into the frigid abyss from whence it came.

Fred L. Whipple of the Harvard-Smithsonian Center for Astrophysics describes a comet as nothing more than a solid mass of ice and gravel. He calls it a dirty iceberg. Whipple's model is widely accepted by other scientists, even though the iceberg nucleus of a comet is far too small to be seen from Earth. Until one of the space probes to Halley gets a peek at its nucleus, the dirty iceberg exists only in theory. But its reality seems likely since it best explains how solar energy impinging on that blob of ices a few miles in diameter melts its outer layers and produces the visible phenomenon. Today astronomers only infer the nature of the heart of a comet. No one knows for sure precisely what it is.

Analysis of the paths of hundreds of comets indicates that they are all part of the solar system. Every known comet orbits the sun, although most of them move in extremely elongated ellipses, some with periods of millions of years. Most comets spend the bulk of their lives far beyond the orbit of the most distant planet, Pluto.

No known comet has come cruising in on an open (hyperbolic) orbit, which would indicate that it originated among the distant stars. If one had, scientists would be even more interested in them than they are now because such interstellar visitors could then represent material billions of years older than our solar system. In theory, some interstellar comets must exist. The orbits of several comets are known to have been dramatically altered by the gravitational attraction of the planets, particularly the giants Jupiter and Saturn. A few of these

3

comets were kicked out of the solar system on trajectories that will carry them on infinite cruises through the galaxy. So far, though, not one such traveler ejected from another star system has been observed in our solar system.

Comet ejection in reverse best explains the orbits of about 120 comets—including Halley—whose orbits take less than 200 years to navigate. Thousands of years ago Halley came booming toward the sun when a chance pass near one of the larger planets shunted it into an orbit with a current period of 76 years. We know Halley has been looping around this gravitational racetrack for at least 2000 years. It has been observed on all but one return to the sun since 240 B.C. Because few people's lives span the comet's orbital period, the idea that it could be the same comet had to wait until 1705 and Edmund Halley's publication of the paths of comets dating back to 1337.

Halley reported that three comets—those of 1456, 1531 and 1607—had roughly the same orbit as the comet of 1682, which he had seen as a young man. He concluded that they were all the same object. "It would be next to a miracle if there were three different comets," he wrote. He then went on to boldly predict that it would appear again in 1758. Halley didn't live to see his prediction vindicated on Christmas night 1758, proving once and for all that comets are members of the solar system with their own orbits about the sun.

More has been written about Halley's Comet than about all the others combined—and with good reason. It was Halley that England's King Harold saw in 1066. He took it as an ill omen. For him, it was. He lost his crown and his life to William the Conqueror at the Battle of Hastings that same year. The whole affair is chronicled in the Bayeux Tapestry—including the comet, which looks like a sphere with a flare jutting out one side.

Roman Emperor Nero—who murdered most of his family, including his mother, set Rome afire and massacred the children of condemned men--survived the visit by Halley in 66 A.D. But two trips later, in 218, Halley was recorded as "a fearful flaming star" that preceded the death of Emperor Macrinus of Rome. The same fate awaited Attila when the great comet swooped by again in 451. As recently as 1910, the comet's latest return, it was only last-minute intervention by authorities that prevented the sacrifice of a young Oklahoma girl by a demented sect called the Select Followers, who were trying to save their souls from the evil vapors of the comet.

No, civilization has not entirely quelled the active minds of those who want to believe that comets and disaster go hand in hand. On the night of May 18, 1910, astronomers predicted that the Earth would pass through the tail of Halley's Comet. They assured the public that the very most that could happen would be a shower of harmless meteors, but even that was unlikely. They noted that the Earth had passed through the tail of a comet in 1861 without apparent ill effects. However, during an interview with a Yerkes Observatory astronomer, a Chicago newspaper reporter learned that deadly cyanogen gas was discovered in the gaseous tail of a comet seen in 1908. His article the next day started a rumor maelstrom.

To counter the new rumors that poisonous gases would soon engulf the Earth, a Professor McHugh of DePauw University made the following statement at a press conference: "None of the gases in the comet will come closer than, say, 45 miles to the Earth's surface. At that distance, the Earth's atmosphere is much more dense than the tail of the comet." But it was too late.

According to The New York Times of May 18, 1910: "Terror occasioned by the near approach of

Halley's Comet has seized hold of a large part of the population of Chicago. Especially has the feminine portion succumbed. Comets and their ways and habits are the principal topic discussed in the streets, cars and elevated trains today."

Details of the classic comet rip-off were chronicled in a Galveston, Texas, newspaper under the headline BIG TRADE IN COMET PILLS—TWO SLICK CROOKS SWINDLE TEXANS:

"Two men who sold hundreds of comet pills and mouth inhalers to superstitious Texans in four counties of South Texas were arrested yesterday. The authorities had clear cases against the men for swindling, but the courthouse was soon beseiged by people begging for the release of the men. The victims pleaded they had not been swindled, that the time for the world to be destroyed had now arrived and that to punish these men would surely bring dire results to anyone who would appear against them. Unable to secure witnesses, the officials decided to hold them for vagrancy. The victims had paid from $5 to $24 for leather inhalers that were to be worn when asleep to protect against the poisonous gases of the comet's tail. Some had bought as many as fifty of the outfits. Hundreds of pills of sugar and quinine were also sold. The two men claiming to be from Ohio had many agents working and collected several thousand dollars."

In Kentucky, groups expecting the world to end gathered in all-night church services "praying and singing to prepare themselves to receive the celestial visitor and meet their doom," reported a Lexington newspaper. Charlatans were selling comet pills in many rural areas as fast as they could make them. Seizing on the rising hysteria, a practical joker had some fun the night before the Earth passed through Halley's tail. Here is the newspaper report from May 18, 1910:

"Comet watchers of Roselle, New Jersey, were thrown into a state of terror last night as the result of the practical joke of Arthur Smith, a chemist, of that place. Knowing that the residents of the town were on the lookout for any phenomena that might result when the Earth passed through the tail of the comet, Smith, with the aid of a small balloon, a quantity of sodium, a time fuse and a stick of dynamite, contrived an apparatus which would rise into the air to a height of 1000 feet and then explode with a terrific roar, igniting the sodium, which would fall to the ground in a great shower of flame. Smith, accompanied by his son, took the apparatus to a large vacant field in the south section of the town. It was released and worked to perfection. The explosion of the dynamite could be heard for miles. Fully an hour passed before fears of the people were allayed."

In South Africa a group of entrepreneurs built an airtight brick chamber complete with cylinders of oxygen for protection against the supposed noxious fumes from the gases in the comet's tail. They reportedly sold a good number of $50 tickets. Elsewhere in South Africa, the wealthy owner of a large mining company built a shelter for his family in one of the deepest mine shafts. His wife took up residence for several days around the comet's closest approach to Earth.

Similar craziness undoubtedly accompanied each of the comet's returns to Earth. Comet specialist Donald Yeomans of NASA's Jet Propulsion Laboratory, Pasadena, Calif., says Halley probably looked much the same thousands of years ago as it did in 1910. Judging from historical documents of comet sightings, he concludes that "the comet's ability to outgas has remained relatively constant."

Using records of sightings of Halley back to 240 B.C., Yeomans, along with Tao Kiang of Dunsink

Observatory, Northern Ireland, developed a computer program that was able to calculate the perihelion (closest approach to the sun) passages of Halley back to 1404 B.C. They couldn't go farther back because the comet made a close pass by the Earth that year. Due to the uncertain distance of that close approach, the gravitational influence on Halley's orbit is impossible to pin down, making it difficult to determine its precise orbit before 1404 B.C.

Yeomans says there are no definite observations of Halley in any historical records prior to 240 B.C. This is probably because good observing conditions only occurred in 1266 B.C. and 1404 B.C., and neither of these was as favorable as 1910. However, for the 29 apparitions from 240 B.C. to 1910, the comet was plainly visible in a dark sky 14 times, and eight of these were comparable to 1910. One of these good passes occurred in 164 B.C., but curiously, no observations of that approach of Halley have been uncovered so far.

Orbital calculations by Yeomans and Kiang show that Halley's period has varied due to the gravitational influences of the planets from 68.15 years in 1266 B.C. to a maximum of 79.29 years in 451 A.D. The comet's period has remained between 76 and 78 years since 1378. Its closest approach to Earth was a mere four million miles on April 11, 837 A.D. The comet was as bright as Venus that night.

Some day, perhaps during the lifetime of people alive today, a human will walk on Halley's Comet. It will probably happen out near the orbit of Jupiter, where sunlight is too feeble to get the comet's vapors percolating. The comet's icy nucleus is likely a craggy, irregularly shaped object about three or four cubic miles in size, pitted and fissured by gases expelled from within during its previous trips near the sun.

The 50-billion-ton celestial flying mountain is only

RETURNS TO PERIHELION OF HALLEY'S COMET

(Calculations by Donald K. Yeomans and Tao Kiang)

1986	Feb.	9	Due to return
1910	Apr.	20	Feverishly publicized and widely observed; bright, prominent
1835	Nov.	16	Widely observed but fainter than 1910
1759	Mar.	13	Halley predicted this return
1682	Sept.	15	Seen by Halley
1607	Oct.	27	Observed by Kepler
1531	Aug.	26	Recorded in Europe and elsewhere
1456	June	9	Numerous recorded sightings
1378	Nov.	10	Numerous recorded sightings
1301	Oct.	25	Numerous recorded sightings
1222	Sept.	28	Numerous recorded sightings
1145	Apr.	18	Numerous recorded sightings
1066	Mar.	20	Depicted on Bayeux Tapestry
989	Sept.	5	Numerous recorded sightings
912	July	18	Numerous recorded sightings
837	Feb.	28	Numerous recorded sightings
760	May	20	Numerous recorded sightings
684	Oct.	2	Numerous recorded sightings
607	Mar.	15	Chinese records
530	Sept.	27	European records
451	June	28	Observed in China and Europe
374	Feb.	16	Chinese records
295	Apr.	20	Chinese records
218	May	17	Chinese records
141	Mar.	22	Chinese records
66	Jan.	25	Chinese records
12 B.C.	Oct.	10	Suggested omen for the death of Agrippa

87 B.C.	Aug.	6	Recorded by Chinese; seen by Julius Caesar
164 B.C.	Nov.	12	No records
240 B.C.	May	25	Existing Chinese records indicate the comet was watched—earliest recorded sighting
315 B.C.	Sept.	8	
391 B.C.	Sept.	14	
466 B.C.	July	18	
540 B.C.	May	10	
616 B.C.	July	28	
690 B.C.	Jan.	22	
763 B.C.	Aug.	5	
863 B.C.	May	9	
911 B.C.	May	20	
986 B.C.	Dec.	2	
1059 B.C.	Dec.	3	
1129 B.C.	Apr.	3	
1198 B.C.	May	11	
1266 B.C.	Sept.	5	
1334 B.C.	Aug.	25	
1404 B.C.	Oct.	15	Earliest date which can be calculated with reasonable accuracy

one-billionth the mass of Earth's moon. Its weak gravitational attraction means that just the slightest push by an explorer's big toe would send him hurtling dozens of feet off the surface. A day on the Halley iceberg is about 50 hours long—its rotation period. The spin axis is likely vertical, like Earth's.

For 75 of its 76-year orbit, Halley's Comet remains in hibernation. Only in the year of a close approach to the sun do things begin to happen. Very subtly at first, a tenuous mist would begin to envelop the body as some exposed ice (mostly frozen water) sublimates. This would probably signal the time to return to Earth for any exploration team—or at least to get off the surface and observe the nucleus from a distance. Once inside the orbit of Mars, the comet releases several hundred tons of dust and gas per minute. The Halley iceberg might then become a dangerous place for an earthly explorer.

When the results of the spacecraft and Earth-based explorations of Halley in 1985-86 are complete, we will undoubtedly uncover completely unsuspected phenomena. But the quest will not be complete until humans walk on the famous icy visitor that mystified our ancestors for so long.

2
Watching For Halley

The view of Halley's Comet from Earth in 1985-86 will be far less impressive than it was in 1910. Comet expert John C. Brandt bluntly labels the viewing circumstances as "terrible." Anyone expecting to see a glowing tail arching across the sky will almost certainly be disappointed. An elongated smudge will be the likely appearance to the unaided eye—at least from the U.S.A.

One of the most authoritative estimates of Halley's expected performance emerged from a detailed examination of historical records of the comet's brightness over the past two millennia, made by Peter Broughton of the Royal Astronomical Society of Canada. Broughton has calculated that the upcoming performance of Halley's Comet will be its worst ever. He says American sky-watchers will be lucky if the comet becomes bright enough to be easily noticed with the unaided eye.

Since astronomers were so far off with their predictions of grandeur for the lackluster Comet Kohoutek in 1973, there would seem to be a hope that they could be equally off the mark in the opposite sense with this pronouncement about Halley's Comet. But Broughton says this situation is different. His confidence in predicting the disappointing return of Halley's Comet in 1986 stems from the comet's previous appearances, which provide a reliable benchmark. "We know far more about Halley than we know about Kohoutek or any other comet," says comet expert Brian Marsden of the Harvard-Smithsonian Center for Astrophysics, Cambridge, Mass. "The Halley predictions are solidly based."

Why will Halley fizzle this time around? Like all comets, Halley's giant oval orbit has the sun near one end, while the other extends into deep space. At the far end of its orbit, Halley is out beyond the orbit of Neptune, more than three billion miles from the Earth and sun. We see the comet at its best when it is less than Earth's distance from the sun, when solar radiation is producing the longest tail.

At such times, we normally get a ringside view of Halley, but only if the comet is on the same side of the sun as we are. And that's the problem in 1986. The comet will be on the far side of the sun when it puts on its best show. Not only will Halley be much farther away from us than in 1910 but also the sun will obscure the view during the prime time. We have reservations for a seat behind the post.

Another factor working against us is the brightness of the sky. Back in 1910 you could see the Milky Way from the downtown area of almost any city. Brilliant lighting in shopping plazas, industrial parks, offices and homes was nonexistent early in this century. But now, faced with today's artificial illumination of the sky, the dim comet will be difficult to see from in or near any urban area. Furthermore, Halley's orbit is tipped so that when it is at its brightest, it will be well seen from the southern hemisphere but below the horizon from most of the U.S. It all adds up to a disappointing performance for backyard astronomers.

Accepting these gloomy prognostications, what exactly can you expect to see? If you watch from the city or a well-lit urban area, Halley will almost certainly be invisible to the unaided eye—washed out by civilization. From such locales, binoculars may serve to identify Halley, but it may not be easy. *The first rule of comet watching is to* load your binoculars or telescope in the car and *go to the darkest, highest . site you can find.* Higher elevations are essential to give you a clear view of the horizon. Comets—including Halley—are often at their best when seen hugging the horizon at dusk or dawn. When a comet is positioned high in the sky it is generally farther from the sun and therefore less bright.

Now for some comet nomenclature. To the unaided eye or through a small telescope, comets appear to have an almost starlike core, or *nucleus*, surrounded by a misty haze called the *coma*. Some comets have ill-defined nuclei, appearing simply as a compact blob of nebulous material gradually fading off toward the edges. (The nucleus referred to here is not the icy body of the comet itself, also called the nucleus, but the apparent nucleur core of the comet. Astronomical tradition perpetrates the confusion in using the same term for both.)

The *tail* of the comet is almost always noticeably fainter than the coma and visually shows little structure. Most comets have two distant types of tails, a *dust tail* and a *gas tail*. The dust tail is highly reflective in wavelengths visible to the human eye and is the one you notice when observing a comet. The visually less prominent gas tail is caused by the solar wind—a flow of particles spewed out from the sun at one million miles per hour, carrying ionized gas and trapped magnetic fields deep into space. As the solar wind strikes the expanding atmosphere of a comet's coma, it ionizes some of the molecules by high-energy electron impacts. The entangled magnetic fields carry these ions back into the tail like a magnetic fishnet that enfolds charged particles but lets the neutral ones flow through. Photos that show knots, loops and strands in the tail are picking up this gas tail, thus revealing detail which the eye seldom sees.

A dusty comet is the most prominent visually. (Comet Kohoutek was low on dust, hence faint to the eye.) The brightest comets sometimes brandish length-wise striations, like strands of hair. The ancient description from which our word comet is derived, "ko-metes," is Greek for wearing long hair.

Halley will appear gray or perhaps yellowish-white, if it is bright enough to see colors at all. Color photographs will record the dust tail as yellow and the gas tail white or bluish. The eye is sensitive to yellow light but relatively insensitive to blue, especially at low light levels.

On previous excursions Halley's tail has extended almost halfway across the sky. But this time if the comet sports a 10-degree tail (equal to the span of the Big Dipper's bowl) it will be a treat for northern-hemisphere skywatchers. Comet specialist Donald K. Yeomans of NASA's Jet Propulsion Laboratory estimates that Halley will be visible in binoculars in the western evening sky as a hazy patch with a small diffuse tail from about mid-November 1985 through to the end of the year, its overall magnitude climbing from about eighth to fifth.

Yeomans says the comet should be just visible to the unaided eye at fourth or fifth magnitude during January, He recommends that Halley watchers always use bin-oculars because of their ability to reveal the subtle

MEASURING BRIGHTNESS:
THE MAGNITUDE SCALE

All astronomical objects have their brightnesses designated in the magnitude scale. The brightest stars are typically first magnitude, those less bright second magnitude, and so on, down to sixth magnitude, the faintest visible to the unaided eye. Binoculars will reveal objects to the eighth magnitude in a dark sky. and small telescopes will get down to tenth or more. A first-magnitude star (or comet) is 100 times brighter than one of sixth magnitude. Objects brighter than first magnitude are designated zero magnitude. After that, the scale goes into negative numbers, –1, –2, etc. The brightest object in the night sky, apart from the moon, is Venus, at –4. The moon itself is –9 at first quarter and –13 when full. A few comets seen in broad daylight have reached magnitude –5 or –6. Halley's maximum brightness was -3 in the year 837 A.D. Estimating a comet's brightness can be tricky due to their difuse rather than starlike appearance. If you defocus your binoulars to make the stars fuzzy blobs like the comet, magnitude comparisons should be easier and more accurate.

extent of the comet's tail. Furthermore, the superior light-gathering power, compared to the eye alone, and the wide field of binoculars allow quick identification of the comet as it treks across the sky from night to night. Yeomans expects Halley's tail will not exceed a couple of degrees before the comet is lost in the sunset glare in late January or early February.

When Halley swings around the sun enough for it to be seen in the eastern morning sky during the last half of March 1986, it will have a longer tail due to solar cooking, but Yeomans says the comet is unlikely to exceed fourth magnitude. Following this brief morning-sky appearance, the comet's orbit carries it back into the evening sky where it will slowly climb above the south-eastern horizon from mid-April through to the summer. This final view of Halley will see it decline from an estimated fifth magnitude to invisibility, except in good-sized telescopes, by late July.

So, according to the experts, the best we can expect is a good binocular comet but a weak performance for the unaided eye. Although it is extremely improbable that Halley will deviate substantially from these predictions, there is always the chance that a burst of activity will give the famous comet a boost in brightness for a few days after it rounds the sun. It happened in 1836. Ten weeks after perihelion (closest approach to the sun), the comet surged from fifth to second magnitude in two days, then slowly subsided. This was likely due to the release of a pocket of volatile gas, which spewed a healthy supply of dust into the coma and tail.

Other comets have had even more violent jumps in brightness, probably resulting when solar radiation melt-ed through to expose a really substantial pocket of volatiles. In 1973 a faint comet named Tuttle-Giacobini-Kresak increased in brightness 10,000 times over a period of just a few nights, then subsided to its original level. Such bursts are rare, but if you happen to be observing a comet and notice it is much brighter than the night before, it's a substantial discovery.

In general, however, no comet, including Halley, is impressive until it exceeds fifth magnitude. Regardless, once you spot the comet, you should try to observe every clear night. When observing Halley, watch for any structure in the coma. Drawings from the 1836 and 1910 visits show graceful arcs that extended from the nucleus and changed from night to night. These details are almost impossible to photograph. According to Donald Yeomans, during Halley's second-last approach in 1835-36, such drawings have proven highly valuable: "Professional astronomers were all artists to some extent at that time. The size and angles of well-defined features of the comet were measured, and beautifully detailed scale drawings rendered."

Although much larger telescopes were available in 1910, photography had largely replaced visual studies. Yeomans says despite the fact that many photos were taken, the lack of visual studies meant that details of subtle changes near the nucleus were lost because they were overexposed in the photos. Visual studies in 1910, says Yeomans, were, if anything, inferior to those of 1835, even though the comet was perfectly positioned for observation. The few photos that were taken that did not overexpose the inner coma show some fascinating jets and emerging shell structure.

Astronomer E.E. Barnard claimed that in 1910 Halley's visible length exceeded 120 degrees. The actual length of the tail may have reached 80 million miles at maximum and was at least 10 million miles long for about a month after perihelion. Halley was first seen during the 1910 apparition on September 11, 1909, at about 15th magnitude and 3.5 AU from the sun. The last photo was taken May 30, 1911, at Lowell Observatory, with the comet 5.28 AU from the sun, magnitude 18.0 (AU=astronomical unit, the distance from Earth to sun.)

With the comet so poorly positioned this trip, it will be more difficult to detect the type of inner coma structure seen during the last two appearances. Just as interesting as the specific details of the comet are the changes in overall size, shape and brightness from night to night as it slowly shifts its position against the starry background. These are easier to note and worthwhile for astronomy enthusiasts to record. A page for recording these observations is provided in this book.

Although Halley's Comet itself can only be seen for a few months of its 76-year period, it leaves a ghostly remnant in our sky that can be viewed every year. Littering the path that Halley traces around the sun are millions of tons of debris in the form of dust fallout, partly dispersed from the tail, partly ejected directly by the activity on the comet's nucleus. The grains range from typical windowsill-dust size to bits about the dimensions of a pea. The Earth comes very close to intersecting Halley's orbit twice as it navigates its annual path around the sun. When Earth sweeps through these swaths of particles, a meteor shower occurs as the particles incinerate due to friction with the upper atmosphere.

The Halley meteor showers are known as the October Orionids and the May Eta Aquarids, named after the sky regions from which the meteors seem to originate—an optical illusion due to perspective. Donald Yeomans has predicted a maximum of the Orionid shower on the night of October 23-24, 1985, and for the Eta Aquarids, the night of May 7-8, 1986. These should be the best showings for these showers in many years. However, you can see debris of Halley's Comet as meteors around these dates every year. Expect to see at least a dozen meteors per hour after midnight. The orientation of the Earth during its daily rotation decreases the number of meteors seen before midnight.

COMET HALLEY: DISTANCE AND BRIGHTNESS
1985-86
(Base data courtesy Donald Yeomans, Jet Propulsion Lab)

Date	Dist. from Earth	Dist. from Sun	Estimated Magnitude	Angular Dist. from Sun
Aug. 1	3.81 AU	3.10 AU	14.3	40.3°
Oct. 1	2.04	2.35	11.3	94.5
Oct. 17	1.53	2.13	10.2	113.3
Nov. 1	1.08	1.92	8.9	136.7
Nov. 11	.82	1.78	7.9	158.8
Nov. 21	.65	1.64	6.9	169.6
Dec. 1	.63	1.49	6.3	132.1
Dec. 11	.75	1.33	6.0	99.6
Dec. 21	.94	1.18	5.8	75.7
Dec. 31	1.14	1.03	5.4	57.2
Jan. 10	1.32	.87	4.8	41.4
Jan. 20	1.47	.74	4.1	26.7
Jan. 30	1.55	.63	3.3	12.9
Feb. 9	1.55	.59	2.9	7.6
Feb. 19	1.45	.62	3.5	20.1
Mar. 1	1.27	.72	4.7	34.5
Mar. 11	1.04	.86	5.0	49.7
Mar. 21	.79	1.00	4.6	67.4
Mar. 31	.55	1.16	4.1	92.3
Apr. 10	.42	1.31	4.0	131.0
Apr. 20	.51	1.47	4.8	147.8
Apr. 30	.77	1.62	6.0	130.3
May 10	1.08	1.76	6.8	115.0
May 20	1.40	1.90	7.5	102.9
May 30	1.73	2.04	8.0	92.5
Jun. 30	2.71	2.46	9.6	65.0
Aug. 30	4.51	3.56	13.6	19.4

AU— distance from Earth to sun

3
Discovering A Comet

According to astronomical tradition, comets are named after their discoverers. Halley's Comet and a few others named after astronomers who unraveled their orbital characteristics are the rare exceptions. This custom has spawned a cult of dedicated amateurs who scan the skies just after dusk or before dawn, when new comets are seen sprouting tails as they approach the sun.

As they gaze through their telescopes, comet hunters dream of the celestial immortality that accompanies the discovery. For many, it is an impossible dream. Luck is a major ingredient: you have to be looking at the right time. One of the world's most persistent comet sleuths has spent hundreds of clear nights over the last 15 years in fruitless pursuit. Six times he has been thwarted by clouds or was not looking in the right place at the right time.

Comet hunters know the sky like a road map of their home towns. They learn how to distinguish the faint glow of multibillion-star galaxies that masquerade as their celestial quarry: a cosmic iceberg just millions of miles, not light-years, distant. Large sectors of the sky are scanned almost every clear night, but comets often elude the eye of the hunter. Instead, they are picked off by professional astronomers engaged in sky photography for other reasons. A major observatory telescope designed for photography can record a comet long before it becomes bright enough for an amateur's scope.

The most prolific American comet hunter of the 20th century was the late Leslie C. Peltier of Delphos, Ohio, who is regarded by many as the outstanding nonprofessional astronomer of modern times. A furniture and toy designer by day, Peltier was a superb telescopic observer who tracked down 12 new comets, even though he spent most of his nights engaged in other astronomical activites.

Tied with Peltier's record of a dozen is Minoru Honda of Japan, who found his first comet in 1940 and eventually inspired a small army of rabid and efficient Japanese comet seekers. Second to Honda among living comet hunters is Australian William Bradfield, an engineer and astronomy hobbyist who has found 11 of the fuzzy interlopers with his 4-inch refractor telescope. Bradfield has chalked up an average of one comet a year since 1970. He spends approximately 160 hours scanning the sky for each comet find.

Using a larger 16-inch telescope, Canadian amateur astronomer Rolf Meier found three comets in less than 100 hours of searching—one of the best comet-discovery records in recent times. His finds were made in 1978, 1979, and 1980. Contrast Meier's experience with England's George Alcock, who scanned the heavens in quest of comets for three years, then, in 1957, found two within a week!

Meier prefers a large telescope for comet seeking, but most comet observers use smaller instruments. After the Second World War, a team of Czechoslovakian comet hunters scored numerous successes with ex-German-army 20-power binoculars with 4-inch objective lenses. Leslie Peltier's dozen comets were caught with a 6-inch telescope at about the same magnification. Low magnification is preferred because it yields the wide field of view necessary for sweeping extended areas of the sky. Smaller telescopes tend to have the widest fields of all, but they sacrifice the larger scopes' ability to detect faint objects. Regardless of the instrument used, the decisive factor is the care and persistence of the observer as he or she thoroughly scans the western sky just after dusk, or the eastern sector before dawn.

The champion comet discoverer of all time was Jean Louis Pons, who bagged at least 30 of the elusive interlopers between 1780 and 1830. (Pons' exact discovery tally by modern standards is uncertain, due to the lax methods of establishing priority at that time.) Pons began his comet-chasing career as a janitor at the Marseilles Observatory. He used a 2-inch refractor of mediocre quality for many of his finds. His outstanding achievement was the independent discovery of five comets in eight months--a feat that has never been duplicated and probably never will be. For one thing, too many comet sleuths are now on the prowl. Also, as mentioned earlier, photographs taken for other purposes often capture faint comets long before an amateur astronomer can see them. (Comet Kohoutek, for example.)

It took Tsutomi Seki, a Japanese comet hunter, 993½ hours of patient scanning with 20x120 binoculars to locate his first comet. California amateur Donald

Macholtz watched at the eyepiece of his 10-inch telescope for over 1700 hours before he bagged his first find. On the average, it requires 100 to 200 hours of diligent, methodical sweeping to capture a comet. However, a 16-year-old Texas schoolboy, Mark A. Whitaker, discovered Comet 1968b on his third night of searching with a 4-inch reflector.

On October 5, 1975, five Japanese astronomers were independently involved in the discovery of two new comets only one hour and ten minutes apart. One of the five, Hiroaki Mori, caught sight of both objects and became the first person ever to be officially credited with discovering two comets in a single night.

To Charles Messier (1730-1817), discovering comets became an obsession. After he found his twelfth comet, his wife fell ill and died. During the last few days of her life, while Messier was taking care of her, he was unable to observe, and a comet was discovered by his rival, Montaigne. After the funeral, when somebody offered condolences on his loss, Messier remarked: "Alas, Montaigne has robbed me of my thirteenth comet." Suddenly realizing his faux pas, he quickly added: "Ah! Poor woman."

In modern times, the comet hunter who has received the most notoriety for his finds is Kaoru Ikeya of Japan. In 1959, at age 16, Ikeya was working in a factory as a lathe operator. His school records labeled him unambitious, and his father had disgraced his family through alcoholism and personal bankruptcy. Ikeya was determined to reverse his fortunes. He had read that discoverers of comets had their names attached to them for all time. For two years he spent all his spare time working on a telescope, building a mount and tube and grinding the mirror. When it was completed, he began a ceaseless program of scanning the night sky for the elongated nebulous patch of an undiscovered comet.

On January 1, 1963, at age 19, Ikeya found a comet and instantly became a national hero. In a country where amateur astronomy has a much higher profile than in the U.S., the disgrace-to-fame story caught the public fancy. Radio and TV crews jostled for interviews. Newspapers gave his discovery banner headlines. An abandoned water tower in Ikeya's home town was transformed at public expense into an observatory dome for his personal use. Eventually, Ikeya discovered two more comets (including Ikeya-Seki of 1965, one of the brightest of the 20th century) and became a widely known personality. A film based on his life has been shown many times on Japanese television.

In an average year, less than a dozen comet hunters are rewarded with a find. When a comet is discovered, it usually remains visible only in telescopes or binoculars. A naked-eye comet makes an appearance every two or three years. About once a decade the skies are visited by a bright comet with a distinct naked-eye tail. Only three or four times a century does a really spectacular comet enter our solar system. These marvels may become so bright (like Ikeya-Seki) that they are visible in the daytime sky. This is the bounty that all comet hunters dream about.

Telescope manufacturers dream about bright comets too. According to comet historians Michael Oppenheimer and Leonie Haimson: "More telescopes were reportedly sold in the three months before Halley's arrival in 1910 than in the entire period following the Civil War. Many of the buyers set up their telescopes on the roofs of their apartments or houses. On April 23 one of them received an unanticipated bonus when, observing at night, he spotted a burglar trying to break into his brother's apartment."

When Halley's Comet became visible to the unaided eye in late April of 1910, virtually every telescope for sale in the United States had been sold. The same scenario was repeated before Christmas 1973, during the hoopla preceding Comet Kohoutek's swing by the sun. In 1985, as Halley fever mounts, there will be a run on telescopes again. Experienced amateur astronomers, amused by such surges in telescope sales triggered by media hype, know that many people will be persuaded to buy cheap instruments capable of showing little that the sky has to offer. (See "Recommended Reading" for guides on telescopes, and Chapter 9 for recommendations on the best instruments to Halley viewing.)

To keep the annual tally of two dozen or so comets straight, most of which are known comets on return trips the International Astronomical Union has established a system for naming them. The famous Comet Kohoutek, for example, was officially named Comet 1973f ("f" signifies the sixth comet discovered in 1973). As it turns out, the preceding comet, Comet 1973e, was also discovered by Kohoutek. This means there were two Comet Kohouteks in the sky at the same time. To avoid such potential confusion, astronomers long ago adopted the letter system for identifying comets.

Comets are seldom visible for more than the few months around perihelion (closest approach to the sun). The time of perihelion passage can be determined precisely once the comet's orbit is established from accurate observation of its path across the sky. The date of perihelion passage provides a comet with its final designation for the record books. Comet Kohoutek 1973f is now known as Comet 1973XII, the twelfth comet to pass perihelion that year.

If you think you have discovered a comet, don't phone anyone. A phone call alone is not proof of discovery. Send a telegram immediately to the Central Bureau for Astronomical Telegrams, Harvard-Smithsonian Center for Astrophysics, Cambridge, Mass. (TWX

710-320-6842 ASTROGRAM CAM), and follow it up the next day with a phone call during working hours or a letter (60 Garden St., Cambridge, MA 02138). The time of the telegram's dispatch is your priority insurance. Be sure to include the suspected comet's position, brightness and direction of motion, if obtained. But be warned that most reports of comet "discoveries" are misidentifications of nebulas, galaxies, "flares" of reflected light in the the telescope optics or previously discovered comets. The first three observers who spot a comet before word of its existence is disseminated have their names attached to it. It's a prize for a lifetime.

4
Great Comets of the Past

Despite popular opinion to the contrary, Halley is not the brightest comet of all time, nor even of the 20th century. The great comet's notoriety is due to the fact that it is by far the brightest comet that has returned on many occasions within historical times, each reprise spanning about three generations.

During its last swing by the Earth in 1910, Halley's Comet was, at its best, an impressive sight rivaling the brightest stars in overall luminosity. Through a bizarre quirk of cosmic fate, an even brighter comet graced the skies in January 1910, only a few months before Halley's long-heralded appearance. Many people who later described Halley's visit in glowing terms actually saw the January comet, which was so bright that it was discovered in broad daylight by three South African diamond miners on their way home from work. Soon after its discovery, when the comet moved into the night sky, its filmy tail, extending for more than a hand span, arched above the western horizon at dusk. Four months later Halley reached naked-eye visibility, making 1910 by far the banner year for comets in this century.

The other great daylight comet of this century, Ikeya-Seki, appeared in 1965 and was an impressive sight from south of the latitude of Los Angeles or Atlanta. Ikeya-Seki's long delicate tail was seen curving up from the eastern horizon just before sunrise in November 1965. But such sights are rare. Normally comets are unimpressive objects, only visible with the aid of a telescope. Appearing like faint stars embedded in mist, their tails are often nothing more than a weak fan of haze pointing away from the sun.

One of the difficulties in establishing an inventory of the truly great comets of history is the unreliability of the descriptions prior to about 1750, when both astronomers and historians were often roused to exaggeration by the cosmic spectacle. It is easy to forget that in the 16th century and earlier, comets were regarded with genuine fear, since their nature was a total mystery and their antics unlike anything else seen in the night. For example, a comet seen in 146 B.C. was described by Seneca: "[it was] as large and fiery as the sun and dispelled the darkness of the nights."

There are several other references from about 2000 years ago of comets that rivaled the brilliance of the full moon or lit up the night sky enough to cast shadows. It is not impossible for a comet to be a shadow-casting phenomenon, perhaps as bright as magnitude -9. If such comets did appear to our ancestors, then they exceeded anything seen in recent times.

British comet historian Peter Lancaster Brown says that probably the most reliable ancient record of a truly spectacular comet concerns the Great Comet of 1264.

Chinese and European astronomers watched it for over four months, recording a tail that at one point extended more than halfway across the sky.

Other comets described with unbridled expletives by historical writers were seen in 1106, 1402, 1472, 1532 and 1577. The last of these was carefully observed by the great Danish astronomer Tycho Brahe. Without the aid of the telescope, which had not yet been invented, Brahe carefully measured the comet's position and, by simple triangulation, determined that it had to be more distant than the moon. Previous to this, comets were generally regarded as nearby atmoshperic phenomena, which explains some of the dread they inspired for so long. Just how any of these comets compared with, say, the January Comet of 1910 or Halley is difficult to say.

The first comet descriptions that can be treated with some semblance of comparative reliability are those of the Klinkenberg-De Cheseaux Comet of 1744, which displayed a fanned peacock-like tail distinctly divided into at least six components. This comet was bright enough for astronomers to observe its nucleus by telescope in broad daylight.

The Great Comet of 1811 gained much of its historical prominence because it was perfectly placed for northern-hemisphere observers. It was visible to the naked eye for 17 months, an all-time record, which leads some comet aficionados to proclaim it the finest ever seen.

The 19th century was the century of two magnificent sun-grazers—comets that sweep close enought to the solar fires to have their surfaces boiled off in churning fury, thrusting vast clouds of dust and gas into an expansive tail. Ikeya-Seki of 1965 has been the only such comet prominently visible in the 20th century. But four of them visited in the 1800s, and three arrived in a clump in 1880, 1882 and 1887. All four comets had almost identical orbits to Ikeya-Seki, and they are probably all related.

If historical records are accurate, an even brighter comet in a similar orbit was seen in 1106. Perhaps all of them are chunks from one colossal sun-grazer that disintegrated. The sun-grazer of 1882 provided supporting evidence of this hypothesis. As it streaked dangerously close to the sun, it broke into five fragments and became known as the string-of-pearls comet. A similar phenomenon was seen in 1965 when a substantial chunk broke away from Ikeya-Seki.

Of the 19th-century sun-grazers, the Great Comet of 1843 was the most sensational. One astronomer reported that the comet's tail stretched over 90 degrees of the sky and was comparable throughout its length to the brightness of the Milky Way. This spectacular tail was intrinsically the longest ever recorded, spanning more than twice the distance from the Earth to the sun. Even more incredible was the fact that the comet survived its passage around the sun, streaking to within 80,000 miles of its surface, less than one-tenth of the sun's diameter. If the sun was not at minimum activity, the comet could have been licked by a solar prominence. Amazingly, it survived the ordeal, brandishing its record-breaking tail as it whisked away from the solar fires. However, the breakup of the 1882 comet suggests that at least some sun-grazers cannot withstand the intense heating on the sunward side of the nucleus during the few hours they are closest to the sun.

Many sun-grazers, including Ikeya-Seki, could be seen in broad daylight simply by placing a hand in front of the sun. The sun-grazer of 1882 was second only to the Great Comet of 1843, but according to the detailed descriptions of many astronomers, it was more impressive than anything seen since. One of the most eloquent descriptions of this object was recorded by the British scientist Sir David Gill:

"There was not a cloud in the sky, but looking due east, one saw the tail of the comet stretching upwards, nearly to the zenith, and spreading with a slight curve. Not a breath stirred; the sky was a dark blue almost to the horizon. The scene was impressive in its solemnity and grandeur. As the comet rose, the widened extremity of its tail extended past the zenith and seemed to overhang the world. When dawn came, the dark blue of the sky near the point of sunrise began to change into a rich yellow, then gradually came a stronger light, and over the mountain and among the yellow, an ill-defined mass of golden glory rose, in surroundings of indescribable beauty. This was the nucleus of the comet. A few minutes after, the sun appeared, but the comet seemed in no way dimmed in brightness, and although in full sunlight the greater part of the tail disappeared, the comet itself remained throughout the day easily visible to the naked eye, with a tail about as long as the moon is broad."

When astronomers learned that the 1882 comet was going to pass directly across the disk of the sun on September 17, no effort was spared in attempts to observe the transit. Anything over 50 miles in diameter would have been seen, but none of the astronomers reported any evidence whatsoever of anything crossing the sun. Four pieces of the 1882 comet are expected to return anywhere between 650 and 950 years from now.

In addition to the sun-grazers, there were two more spectacular comets during the last century. All the old astronomy books vividly report that Donati's Comet of 1858 was one of the finest ever seen. It was visible to the naked eye for 112 days, and at one point its 50-million-mile-long scimitar-shaped tail spanned 64 degrees of the sky. But three years later it was outdone by the Great Comet of 1861, which may have been bright enough to cast a shadow.

On June 30, 1861, the coma of this comet rivaled Venus, and the tail was wide and bright, extending 30 degrees from the sunset horizon like a spreading searchlight beam. During the next few days the tail lengthened to reach a maximum of 118 degrees, the longest apparent length of any comet in recorded history. (The Great Comet of 1843 intrinsically had the longest known tail but was farther from Earth when it was observed.) On June 30 the Earth passed through the comet's tail, the only known instance of this phenomenon other than the Halley incident in 1910.

Comet Brooks of 1911 was another naked-eye comet swallowed up in the Halley ballyhoo of 1910. Skywatchers then suffered a comet drought until 1947, when a fairly impressive celestial visitor navigated the postwar skies. Then another decade passed without substantial comets. Suddenly two naked-eye comets were seen within months of each other in 1957: Comet Arend-Roland in the spring and Comet Mrkos in the fall. Mrkos was independently discovered by airline pilot Peter Cherbak, but records of his find were received too late by the International Astronomical Union for official credit.

Thirteen years after the twin-comet excitement of 1957, and five years after Ikeya-Seki, South African amateur astronomer John C. Bennett discovered a comet that became a fine naked-eye object in the morning skies of April 1970. It was well positioned for northern-hemisphere observers and was the first comet widely photographed in color by amateur astronomers.

Sometimes a comet will become a naked-eye object within a few weeks of its discovery, allowing little time for advance preparation. The opposite was true for

Comet Kohoutek, which was first detected almost a year before its swing past the sun.

Remember Comet Kohoutek? Astronomy buffs salivated as they read predictions describing how it would be the "Comet of the Century"—a blazing spectacle in the January 1974 evening skies, with a dazzling tail beaming up from the western horizon. In total brightness, Kohoutek was supposed to rival the brilliant planet Venus. What actually happened was a far different story. Virtually no one saw the comet except professional and amateur astronomers who knew exactly where to look and what to look for. At its brightest, on January 3, Kohoutek was barely visible to the unaided eye—10,000 times fainter than predictions made only a few months before.

The Comet Kohoutek incident is a perfect example of how much we don't know about comets. Two factors distinguish Kohoutek from most other comets, neither of which was fully accounted for in the brightness estimates. First, Kohoutek was discovered at a huge distance from the sun, 440 million miles away, out near the orbit of Jupiter. Astronomers were amazed to see that the comet was brighter than any comet ever recorded at a comparable distance. Secondly, Kohoutek was definitely a "new" comet, that is, one that never before approached close to the sun.

According to E.J. Opik of Northern Ireland's Armagh Observatory, Comet Kohoutek probably had a surface layer of frozen hydrogen, a pristine remnant from the solar system's formation. Only a slight warming is required to sublimate this rare solid. Thus, even at Jupiter's distance, a hydrogen cloud would form around the comet body itself. Dust grains embedded in the hydrogen would make the cloud an excellent reflector of light. But, of course, no one knew this at the time.

Comet Kohoutek taught us something about the

appearance of comets on their first trip around the sun when seen at great distances. (Such "new" comets account for about five percent of all visible comets.) And Kohoutek did not flop as badly as some other comets in history. Comets Ensor in 1906 and Westphal in 1913 both came streaking toward the sun and flared with impressive bursts of activity. They were predicted to be magnificent objects as they passed the tail-producing heat of the sun. But despite astronomers' desperate searching, both comets were never seen to emerge from their close encounters with the sun.

Comet West of 1976 was one of the great comets of the 20th century. Like Comet Kohoutek, Comet West was discovered by accident when a professional astronomer was examining a photographic plate taken for another purpose. Also like Kohoutek, the calculated orbit revealed that West would come close enough to the sun—within 20 million miles—to produce a fine tail. But more important, it would (again like Kohoutek) be well placed for observation from Earth. All signs pointed to Comet West becoming a splendid naked-eye object.

Because so much of the story resembled the history of Comet Kohoutek, astronomers couched their predictions with an abundance of cautionary adjectives. Newspaper editors were plainly dubious about the new comet, having been burned by heavily promoting Kohoutek as "The Comet of the Century," then watching as it barely gained naked-eye visibility. If anything appeared in print at all, it was always a small item buried in the back pages. Thus few people, apart from astronomy enthusiasts, were even aware of West.

Ironically, Comet West was destined to exceed predictions. Four days before its perihelion passage (closest point to the sun) on February 25, 1976, Comet West surged in brightness from magnitude +3 to -1. The day before perihelion it was seen 10 minutes after sundown at magnitude -2, but because of its nearness to the sun, the full glory of its tail was hidden in twilight.

Sunset on the day of perihelion passage revealed Comet West at magnitude -3. It was seen by some observers *before* sunset. Experienced comet watcher John Bortle has suggested that at that time the comet's appearance was reminiscent of Donati's Comet of 1858-- a small, brilliant nucleus embedded in a bright arc of material swept back into the tail.

Comet West then moved into the morning sky and developed a gorgeous curving tail 15 degrees long. The peak of the display was on the morning of March 7, 1976, when the comet rose in the morning sky with a spectacular fanlike tail that binocular observers saw was composed of at least five separate tails.

The explanation for this burst of activity during West's closest approach to the sun was traced to the comet's nucleus. Between February 12 and March 5, three huge chunks broke away from the nucleus, two of them forming comets in their own right. Apparently, this partial disintegration of the nucleus released enormous quantities of dust and gas, the dust being whisked out into the great fanlike tail. Comet West joined Comet Kohoutek as another example of the unpredictable nature of comets.

Comet West far exceeded the brightness predictions--predictions that were admittedly cautionary. A stupendous comet graced the skies, perhaps second only to Halley and the January 1910 Comet for 20th-century northern-latitude observers. Yet hardly anyone saw it. The fact that West was a morning-sky object was part of the reason. And it was winter. However, the main problem was the reluctance of news editors to talk about Comet West. But, after Kohoutek, who could blame them?

Astronomers will be faced with the opposite scenario in 1985—trying to convince everyone that Halley likely will not be spectacular and may not be visible to the naked eye at all, except from a very dark location. If the real "Comet of the Century" eventually does arrive, let's hope the reaction falls somewhere between hysteria and apathy—call it curiosity.

5
Seeking the Comet Factory

W here did Halley's Comet come from before it was locked into its 76-year track around the sun? And what about the hundreds of other comets that have been seen throughout history? Do they all have a common origin? How many comets are out there that we can't detect? Such questions will carry comet research well into the 21st century.

Aristotle stalled cometary studies for almost 2000 years by proclaiming comets to be atmospheric phenomena, like rainbows or auroras. Although a few other philosophers held different opinions, Aristotle's view was so widely accepted as gospel that few paid any attention to the first observations which suggested he was wrong. Danish astronomer Tycho Brahe, using pretelescopic sighting instruments, proved that a comet seen in 1577 had to lie beyond the moon, otherwise it would have shown a perceptible shift against the background stars when viewed from his observatories at Prague and on the island of Ven, in the Baltic. This idea was so revolutionary that even Galileo couldn't accept it, maintaining that comets were only an illusion created by the effects of sunlight on vapors released from the ground at night.

Aristotle's pronouncement was doubly counterproductive because it overturned the correct notion proposed thousands of years earlier by Chaldean astronomers and later accepted by the Egyptians, who thought that comets were celestial objects that moved in paths like the planets. Picking up on this discarded idea, the Greek philosopher Seneca predicted that "one day there shall arise a man who will demonstrate in what regions of the heavens the comets make their way; why they journey so far apart from the other stars, and what is their nature and size."

Part of Seneca's prophecy was fulfilled by Isaac Newton, who examined the records of sightings of several comets and found that they traveled in long, narrow orbits with the sun at one end. The final proof came with Edmund Halley's successful prediction, that the comet now bearing his name circuits the sun every 76 years.

After Halley solved how and where comets move, the question became how they got there in the first place. Halley's Comet and others with comparable orbital periods couldn't have looped the sun that way since the solar system formed because each pass around our star steams off at least a few hundredths of a percent of a comet's icy body. Halley's trip near the sun in 1985-86 will whisk away 50 million tons of dust and gas into its tail and from there into deep space. At that rate, Halley's life span is less than a thousand trips, or 75,000 years. The supply of comets must constantly be replenished.

From this reasoning emerged the idea that comets originate in some kind of deep-space storehouse. Ernst

Opik, director of the Armagh Observatory in Northern Ireland, was first to suggest this in 1932. A more scientifically rigorous version of this concept was put forward in 1950 by Dutch astronomer Jan Oort. His theory, which is now the prevailing one explaining the origin of comets, is that billions of comets surround the solar system in a colossal cloud extending out perhaps a quarter of the way to the nearby stars, up to 100,000 times the Earth-sun distance.

Oort hypothesized that the comets condensed from the outer portion of the original nebula from which the sun and planets were born. The combined mass of the Oort comet cloud is thought to be between one and 100 times the mass of the Earth, but it could exceed 5000 times the Earth's mass and still remain undetected due to the small size and remoteness of the individual bodies.

The nearest star, Alpha Centauri, is 4.3 light-years away, or about 25 trillion miles. Comets could wander up to two light-years in the direction of Alpha Centauri and still theoretically remain in the sun's gravitational grip. But the galaxy's stars move relative to one another and are constantly passing near enough to us to gravitationally disrupt the fringes of the Oort cloud, dumping some of its members into what ultimately become headlong plunges toward the sun. Millions of years later, these comets swing around the sun for the first time, providing the spectacles that terrified our ancestors and fascinate 20th-century Earthlings.

After the initial pass, a comet will loop back into the Oort cloud on a long, narrow orbit, returning to the sun again in thousands of years. Sometimes a comet's path is deviated by an approach to within a few million miles of a planet. The planet's gravity can rob the comet of some of its orbital momentum, forcing it into a smaller orbit with a period ranging up to a few thousand years. Halley's Comet undoubtedly was pushed into its present orbit in this way. These planetary gravity kicks can also push a comet back into the Oort cloud or oust it from the solar system entirely. If Oort's theory is near the truth, there must be no shortage of comets. To supply comets at the rate we now observe them, there must be at least 200 billion.

Astronomers have prepared elaborate computer "games" that simulate the conditions around the solar system, within a radius of several light-years of the sun, as a way of estimating gravitational effects on the Oort cloud's comets. The games are operated under very strict rules. The planets, the sun and other stars all have their appropriate gravitational influences, and imaginary comets representing random members of the comet cloud fly through trajectories according to the corresponding gravitational forces applied to them by these other objects.

Paul R. Weissman of the Jet Propulsion Laboratory has developed the most elaborate of these computer simulations. By enormously speeding up time to examine the life histories of thousands of sample comets, Weissman has concluded that there are probably even more comets in the cloud than Oort or anyone else estimated— perhaps up to two trillion of them. The vast majority of the cloud's comets never venture within billions of miles of the sun. Regardless of the size of the telescope used for the search, we wouldn't have a hope of seeing the frozen nucleus of a comet at such distances, even if we knew where to look.

The planet Pluto, which is now inside Neptune's orbit and will be until the year 1999, when it begins to loop out beyond Neptune's orbit again (Pluto's orbit is illustrated in the diagram showing the path of Halley's Comet), was discovered after a long and tedious search of literally millions of images on thousands of photographic plates. With a diameter just over half that of Earth's moon, Pluto is by far the smallest planet and, indeed, really doesn't qualify as a planet at all. In fact, it has some curious similarities to what we suspect big comets might be like. Pluto is known to consist almost entirely of ices with perhaps some rocky material mixed in, the same recipe that has been suggested for comets for years. Pluto has a moon of the same composition about half its diameter. The two objects form a double planet or, possibly, a double giant comet.

Pluto could be one of the largest and nearest members of the great comet cloud. Its orbit is far more elliptical than any of the planets, although less elliptical than any comet. One of the two main theories on the origin of the Oort cloud suggests that Pluto may well be some kind of missing link between planets and comets. Both theories agree that comets originated from material left over following the formation of the sun and planets. Where they differ is the location of this debris. The overwhelming favorite a few years ago suggested that the formation occurred at many times Neptune's distance from the sun, far out in the region that would ultimately become the great comet cloud.

The alternative model, which has recently gained in popularity among planetary scientists, proposes that comets are the afterbirth of the formation of the giant planets, especially Uranus and Neptune. In this scenario, billions of comets originally populated the outer fringe of the planetary system. In the first few hundred million years of the solar system's history, this mass of comets was either gravitationally spun out into the comet cloud by close encounters with a giant planet or hurtled by the same mechanism into the inner solar system, where they probably collided with one of the inner planets. Support for this theory is on the upswing because it fits so many observed solar system phenomena.

The Earth, moon and every other solid body in the

solar system was pummeled mercilessly during most of the first billion years of their existence. All the objects in the solar system are believed to be 4.6 billion years old. (The best evidence for this is radioactive dating of the oldest material found on the moon.) Most of the craters on the moon date back to that era, and if it weren't for the weathering effect of air, water, mountain building and continental drift on Earth, the same scars would be here too. (The remains of about a hundred more recent craters have been identified. See Chapter 7.)

The origin of the ancient craters could well be from comet impacts, which occurred when the inner solar system was bombarded as Uranus and Neptune began clearing out their zones by gravitationally flinging comets in every direction. The moons of Jupiter and Saturn show similar cratering records, and one scientist has even suggested that comets colliding with the moons of Saturn produced the spectacular rings around that planet. Planets are fairly effective gravitational vaccum cleaners. If the inner solar system was not constantly being resupplied with comets even today, the planets would have gravitationally swept away virtually all traces of them long ago.

Paul Weissman says his computer simulations cannot distinguish between the two origin hypotheses because comets are now so thoroughly dispersed throughout the Oort cloud by the influence of passing stars that it is impossible to trace their genesis. A "new" comet's rush toward the sun from the cloud can come from any direction, which erases the one way of attacking the problem.

Only a tiny minority of planetary scientists subscribe to the alternative comet-origin theory of British scientist R.A. Lyttleton, which holds that as the sun passes through clouds of interstellar dust and gas in the Milky Way Galaxy, it gravitationally collects enough of this material to form transient comet clouds, such as the one

46

that is now supplying the comets we see. Lyttleton's theory then suggests that the cloud's comet population is replenished as the Earth passes through these nebulosities every 30 million years or so. He says the number of comets in the cloud would therefore vary substantially from one epoch to the next.

Do other stars have comet clouds? There is no fundamental reason why not. But so far, no comet from another star system has been seen in our solar system. Careful measurements of the orbits and velocities of comets on their first trip to the inner solar system have shown that not one of them is moving in a way that indicates it is anything but a member of the sun's family. The evidence to date is overwhelming that comets are part of our solar system and likely represent extremely primordial material dating back to the origin of the system. The fact that many of these objects have remained in a celestial deep-freeze for 4½ billion years makes them exciting targets for future exploration by robot and, ultimately, by manned space probes.

6

Space Missions to Halley's Comet

Ten years ago few would have guessed that all five spacecraft sent to Halley's Comet would be built and launched by countries other than the United States. Not that there weren't imaginative plans. The American assault on Halley was to be bold and dramatic.

But that was a decade ago. By the early 1980s the U.S. Halley exploration plan was in shambles, amounting to little more than a few shelves of loose-leaf binders and computer printouts in the Jet Propulsion Laboratory's mission planning office.

Serious studies for a Comet Halley mission were under way as early as 1973. In those days of annual planetary flybys and landings, blue-sky concepts abounded. It was in such an environment that the solar sail emerged as the ideal carrier of a scientific payload to Halley.

Because the comet orbits the sun in the opposite direction to the Earth, a straightforward launch and intercept with Halley means the spacecraft and comet are approaching head-on. Exotic propulsion systems are required to overcome the velocity differential, thereby achieving a leisurely and scientifically desirable rendezvous. The chemical rockets used for all of today's planetary probes only allow the head-on mission, in which the period of scientific investigation is compressed to minutes—or hours at best—as the instrument-laden vehicle hurtles by the celestial visitor.

The problem faced by trajectory planners is analogous to a passenger in a car attempting to read the fine print on the door of a transport truck while driving down a freeway in the opposite direction. The task is much easier and more productive if the car and truck are both traveling in the same direction. The car simply pulls out and slowly passes the truck, providing ample time for gathering the information.

The solar-sail ideas, conceived to surmount the head-on trajectory disadvantage, envision a vast 160-acre reflective mylar-type sheet held rigid in airless space by extremely lightweight ribbing and guy wires. Propelled merely by solar radiation, which acts much like wind on a boat sail, a solar sail could crank itself around to orbit the sun in the opposite direction from the Earth to match the speed and direction of Halley.

The solar-sail plan was deceptively simple. Small paddles at the corners of the effectively rigid sail were to be used as rudders to allow solar-photon radiation to push the sail in any direction, including away from or toward the sun, just as a sailboat can be tacked at almost any angle. The solar sail is a brilliant scheme. (It was used by science fiction authors long before JPL engineers started seriously toying with the concept.) It represents the ultimate in reaction propulsion systems by virtue of the fact that the total propulsion is derived from external sources. There is no storage of fuel on the spacecraft and, theoretically, no limit to its ability to travel within the solar system.

As attractive as the concept of coasting through space on the solar wind may be, the $500-million to $1-billion price tag for developing and implementing the concept became too rich for NASA's increasingly anemic fiscal blood. By 1977 the Space Agency turned to a less risky and lower-cost alternative mission.

This plan called for two solar-electric-powered spacecraft to fly by Halley in 1986. One of the vehicles would then be retargeted for a flyby of Comet Borrelly in January 1988, while the second robot would proceed to a rendezvous with Comet Tempel 2 in September 1988. Increasing budget storm clouds late in the '70s trimmed the twin-spacecraft idea down to the single Halley/Tempel 2 flight plan, with the Halley encounter in November 1985. That mission called for the main spacecraft to drop a probe to within 300 miles of Halley's nucleus. The main vehicle would then veer away from the comet, much like an aircraft delivering a bomb, passing about 80,000 miles on the sunward side.

The immediate disadvantage compared to the solar sail is that the spacecraft encounters Halley nearly head-on at about 130,000 miles an hour. All the missions now scheduled to meet Halley are on similar direct high-velocity encounters. However, the U.S. plan included the rendezvous with Comet Tempel 2 at low speed. Tempel 2 is a much less active comet than Halley, but the dual-comet concept had many advocates. It was less daring than the solar sail but also less expensive.

But by the end of the 1970s, the pendulum was swinging heavily away from space science. The mission was abruptly scratched in early 1980 when a $20-million request for funds to develop the solar-electric rocket engine needed to propel the probe to the two comets was deleted from the NASA budget. (A solar-electric propulsion system converts sunlight into energy for driving ion rockets. Unlike chemical rockets, ion-drive systems provide continuous thrust.) Without such an exotic and powerful space drive, the three-year dual-comet intercept mission was not feasible.

In retrospect, now that the Soviet, European and Japanese are all going to Halley, the rendezvous with Tempel 2 turns out to be the major casualty. The mission plan envisioned the spacecraft actually going into orbit around the nucleus of that comet, photographing it at extreme high resolution. A year after the rendezvous the robot would spiral in, slowly descending to the surface. Its final readings as it bumped into the icy nucleus would be a determination of the actual physical character and bearing strength of the nuclear material. The Halley/Tempel 2 mission was to carry three cameras—high, medium and low resolution—capable of yielding about 40,000 images of the two comets.

In the final analysis, it seems clear that NASA became comet-shy because of the large number of uncertainties associated with a comet intercept. How well a spacecraft functions within a comet's dust and gas environment is still unknown. Could the instruments get clogged, camera lenses damaged or solar panels made inoperable by dust? How reliably would the new ion engine maneuver the comet probe during several years of tricky trajectory adjustments in the vicinity of two comets? As science writer Ray Villard pointed out at the time the project was cancelled: "There is a built-in catch-22 to this kind of logic. Without first sending a probe to a comet, how can planetary scientists predict what kind of environmental problems are inherent in comet missions?"

Money (about half a billion dollars) and the high risk of sending a new type of spacecraft to a previously unexplored class of object doomed Halley/Tempel 2. Scrambling for alternatives, some NASA scientists suggested sending a conventional spacecraft, possibly even one of the Mariner vehicles built as backups for earlier missions, on a simple high-speed flyby of Halley. But there were arguments about the scientific merit of such a mission, which in many ways would duplicate the European, Soviet and Japanese projects (although there is little doubt that the U.S. spacecraft would send back the most detailed pictures).

Meanwhile, other scientists proposed a completely different approach. They suggested sending a well-protected spacecraft with a single objective: land on Halley, collect a chunk of the comet, blast off and return to Earth orbit, where the sample could be retrieved by the space shuttle. Despite personal appeals to President Reagan by high-powered NASA and aerospace industry officials, none of these missions made it to the Congressional launchpad. It seems that Comet Halley's timing could hardly have been worse as far as the U.S. space program is concerned.

With America out of the Halley encounter sweepstakes, a dual-spacecraft mission mounted by the Soviet Union has become the most elaborate of the robot excursions being hurled from Earth at the icy cosmic cruiser. Historically, Russian space probes to other worlds have not been a match for the electronic wizards that the U.S. has sent to every planet in the solar system except Pluto.

After several failures with their Mars orbiters and landers, the Soviets concentrated on Venus in the last decade, achieving the noteworthy feat of landing seven functioning spacecraft on the sizzling surface, where it is hot enough to melt lead. Color pictures of the landscape on Venus were returned from two spacecraft in 1982, complementing black-and-white images obtained in 1976. But apart from these Venus exploits, Soviet planetary exploration has yielded meager results, compared to the stunning successes of the Mariners, Vikings and Voyagers from America.

The Soviet Halley mission emerged in a curiously serendipitous way while another Venus mission was being planned. The key incident occurred during a conference in France in 1978, where Russian and French scientists were discussing joint experiments to be flown on the next Venus probe.

Since the early '70s, French scientists had expressed interest in dropping balloon-borne instruments into the Venus atmosphere where they could float in the cooler upper levels of the dense carbon-dioxide atmospheric cloak for extended periods, gathering readings of the various gases and wind velocities. Now it finally looked as if the balloons were going to fly on the next Soviet probes to be launched in December 1984 for arrival at Venus in June 1985. The Soviet segment of the new Venus exploration would be another instrument-laden device to be slowed by parachutes for descent to the surface to refine readings from previous landers.

During a cocktail hour after a day of scientific sessions, one of the French astronomers casually mentioned to a Russian scientist how easy it would be to have the main spacecraft carrying the experiment probes to Venus continue on past the planet, loop around the sun and, with some minor trajectory corrections, meet Halley's Comet coming into the solar system from the opposite direction. After drawing some sketches on the back of an envelope, the French scientist was astounded to learn that this idea had never occurred to any of the Russian scientists. They were so excited about it that several of them left the meeting early to return to Moscow to start work immediately on the revisions necessary in spacecraft design to send the vehicle on to Halley.

The Soviet lander, which will drop down onto the nighttime side of Venus in order to facilitate the maneuver to Halley, is still in the mission plan as are the French experiments to go ballooning in the sulfuric-acid rains in Venus' carbon-dioxide atmosphere. French scientists also played a leading role in preparing the scientific instruments for the examination of Halley.

The Soviet vehicles (there will be two identical spacecraft) are equipped with wide- and narrow-angle cameras, basically similar to the ones flown on the Voyager spacecraft, capable of imaging Halley's nucleus down to 1000-foot resolution. American experts say that the high speed of the spacecraft's encounter with Halley might well blur the most detailed pictures. The Soviet cameras will be on a scan platform, which operates something like a motorized tripod head with up-down and left-right motions, similar to the system used on Voyager. This is the first time the Soviets have flown such a sophisticated camera system, one that the U.S. pioneered with its Mars probes almost two decades ago.

Flyby distances from Halley's nucleus will be 6000 miles for the first spacecraft and 2000 miles for the second. The wide berth given the initial craft is planned because of uncertainties in estimating the threat of spacecraft damage from impact by cometary debris. If the Soviet mission goes as planned, the first spacecraft will arrive March 6, 1986, the second to follow three days later.

The probe will use charge-coupled-device, or CCD, cameras, which have much higher sensitivity than the vidicon cameras used in earlier U.S. and Soviet space missions. The wide-angle camera will have a field of view up to 5.2 degrees in width, depending on the amount of the frame transmitted back to Earth. The flood of information during the encounter means that in some cases, only the brightest part of the frame will be returned to allow other data to be transmitted. This restriction also applies to the 0.4 degree narrow-angle camera.

The spacecraft will measure dust densities, dust-particle sizes and charged particles (plasma) surrounding the comet. The camera is capable of photographing the nucleus in the near infrared, which should be able to cut through a substantial portion of the suspected dust cloud that will be emerging from the nucleus at the time of the encounter. French and Hungarian scientists are collaborating with the Soviets on the imagery experiments, and East German and Bulgarian researchers have been involved with other experiments. The French are the major collaborators in the mission.

The European Space Agency's Halley probe, named Giotto after the artist who adorned the Arena Chapel at Padua with an image of the comet seen in 1301, will be a kamikaze mission plunging through the coma to within 300 miles of the nucleus. A double skin on its nose will protect Giotto from the sandblasting effect of comet dust during the initial phases of the 140,000 mph close encounter.

But scientists are doubtful that the little craft will survive the four-hour ordeal. In addition to the dust's high-speed abrasion, leading to eventual spacecraft damage, the rain of particles will deflect the vehicle in the way a severe crosswind influences an airplane. Although spin-stabilized like a top, the spacecraft's orientation momentum will likely be overcome within 1200 miles of the nucleus, and communication with Earth will be lost. For this reason (among others), data from Giotto will be transmitted to Earth in real time.

Giotto will be launched in July 1985, in tandem with another spacecraft, by the European Ariane rocket. Intercept with Halley is planned for March 13, 1986, a month after the comet's perihelion passage. The European Space Agency (a consortium of 11 nations) will spend $145 million on Giotto, which is less than half the price tag of any of the abandoned U.S. missions.

Like the USSR Venus/Halley craft, Giotto will be equipped with charge-coupled-device optics, the most advanced imaging system available. However, the spin-stabilized system selected by the Europeans permits far less photography than the more sophisticated three-axis stabilized craft, such as the new Soviet craft and the U.S. Mariner, Viking and Voyager robots used throughout the 1970s. Nevertheless, if photographs of the nucleus are obtained from as close as 1200 miles, they will yield 150-foot resolution and reveal barn-sized objects on the nucleus. When the spacecraft is closer, the images will be seriously smeared by the robot's high velocity relative to Halley.

Besides high-resolution imaging of Halley's nucleus, other experiments on Giotto will analyze the composition of comet particles and the primarily hydrogen cometary atmosphere. A plasma analyzer and magnetometer will characterize the plasma environment around the comet, and an impact detector will determine the size and density of particles in the comet's coma and tail. The Europeans hope the pictures will show the size, shape and texture of the icy nucleus as well as its rotation and the manner in which the comet expels material to produce the coma and streaming tail.

For their first venture into deep space, Japanese scientists have also selected Halley as their target. Two small spacecraft, each weighing 300 pounds, will be separately launched by a new Japanese rocket on December 31, 1984, and August 14, 1985. The first vehicle will be a distant observer, never swinging closer to Halley than about 10 million miles. But while it is examining the comet from the bleachers, the companion robot will zoom in like the Russian probes for a close encounter on March 8, 1986.

All five spacecraft to Halley will arrive during March, the month of expected peak cometary activity after closest approach to the sun. The Japanese are concentrating on ultraviolet imagery, which should tell something about the density and composition of the nucleus, the hydrogen coma and the tail of Halley.

Unless the Russians have substantially improved their past performance in obtaining and processing images, the best pictures should come from Giotto. Ironically, a camera system with exquisite sensitivity and flexibility will be launched by the space shuttle in another direction and several months too late. The cameras are those of Galileo, a spacecraft destined to orbit Jupiter and deposit a probe into the giant planet's atmosphere. Galileo's cameras are an improvement over the two Voyagers'. (Remember what a spectacular job they did?) Galileo could have been launched earlier and targeted to pass within 15 million miles of Halley, close enough for superbly detailed pictures of its coma and tail. But such a diversion, besides costing about $50 million would delay arrival at Jupiter.

The 94-inch Space Telescope, to be placed in Earth orbit by the shuttle in late 1986, will be the most powerful telescope available for viewing the comet after it leaves our part of the solar system. The orbiting scope's ultrasensitive instrumentation is expected to allow viewing of the comet's retreat well beyond Saturn's orbit--a far greater distance than any other comet has been observed.

During 1985-86 the space shuttle will carry Spacelab, a flying laboratory of telescopes and detectors that will be able to probe Halley in energy regions invisible to ground-based instruments because of the absorbing and reflecting properties of the Earth's atmosphere. Several Spacelab missions are planned to coincide with prime Halley viewing periods. And backing all this up, of course, will be thousands of telescopes in backyards and observatories around the globe.

7
Comet Catastrophies

On the morning of June 30, 1908, in a remote region of Siberia, the sky was sliced by a dazzling fireball more brilliant than the sun. The fiery apparition plummeted like a flaming spear toward a collision with the Earth, but just before reaching the ground, it exploded in a blinding flash of smoke and fire.

The searing heat of the detonation scorched the shirt of a farmer standing on his porch 40 miles away. Seconds later a deafening shock wave hurled him to the ground, knocking him unconscious. Trees were felled like matchsticks for 20 miles around the blast site, and seismometers hundreds of miles away went wild.

Evidence painstakingly accumulated decades after this remarkable event strongly suggests that the exploding object was a small comet, about the size of a 15-story apartment building. Czechoslovakian astronomer Lubor

Kresak is convinced that the baby comet was a chip off the old block of ice we call Comet Encke. No crater or fragment of the impacting body has ever been found. The comet chunk exploded before reaching the surface. But why?

Like all comets, the Siberian object was a rubbly conglomerate of ice, dust and gravel that can break up under the pressure of the atmospheric shock front created during a plunge toward the ground. Once the intruder began to disintegrate, it was almost instantaneously vaporized, producing the colossal explosion.

Yet by cosmic standards, the 1908 comet was a mere pebble. Halley's Comet is a million times more massive. Sooner or later the Earth will be clobbered by a Halley-sized cometary mass. Although the Earth's atmosphere caused the disintegration of the Siberian comet, it would be like baby's breath on a mass as great as Halley. The impact of such a gigantic flying mountain of ice and rubble would produce a greater catastrophe than an all-out nuclear war. The scenario is awesome:

If the comet crashed into the ocean, it would vaporize thousands of cubic miles of water and throw up a tidal wave as high as the Rocky Mountains, which would surge hundreds of miles onto the surrounding continents. If it hit land, the comet would be blasted to vapor in less than a second, creating an explosion equal to a million times the energy of the great San Francisco earthquake—enough to knock down every building on Earth. In either case, a 100-mile-wide crater would be ripped open, with much of the excavated material ejected hundreds of miles farther.

Enough dust and debris (600 trillion tons) would be thrown into the air to cover the globe half an inch deep. The finer material would remain suspended, blocking sunlight and turning day into night for months. Because of the heat of the explosion, temperatures would initially rise at least 10 degrees worldwide, then fall due to reduced sunlight. If that isn't enough to wipe out most life on Earth, the gases from the comet's vaporized ices would contain cyanide and sulfur compounds lethal to many plants and animals.

NASA astronomer John O'Keefe predicts that such an event occurs every few hundred million years. Statistically, this fits with what is known about Earth's history. Dozens of craters ranging up to 100 miles across have been identified on Earth. Some are hundreds of millions of years old. Bombardment from space is an established scientific fact.

Recently, however, strikingly persuasive evidence of another kind has been uncovered suggesting that either a comet or an asteroid smashed into the Earth 65 million years ago. "In the last 500 million years, there have been several major extinctions," says paleontologist Dale Russell of the Canadian National Museum of Natural Sciences in Ottawa. "The most severe occurred 65 million years ago when three-quarters of all plant and animal species became extinct, including all the dinosaurs. Something catastrophic happened."

The chain of discoveries began when University of California geophysicist Walter Alvarez was in Italy in 1977 examining a stratum of rock that was laid down at the time the dinosaurs disappeared. Paleontologists had known for years that this layer contained hardly any fossils of living creatures as compared to the older layers below, which belong to the dinosaurian era. But Alvarez wanted to determine the time span during which the population and the variety of living creatures on Earth were severely depleted.

To define the method of approach, he sought the assistance of his father, Luis Alvarez, a nuclear physicist at the University of California's Berkeley campus. They decided to measure the amount of meteoric material in the sample. Since meteors rain into the Earth's atmosphere at a constant rate of 100,000 tons a year, they knew that the abundance of meteoric dust would indicate the length of time it took for the soil to be deposited.

Meteor dust is relatively rich in elements such as iridium, osmium and platinum, which are rare in normal Earth soil. Of these, the easiest to detect is iridium. When the experiment was completed, they were amazed to find the iridium levels 30 times higher than expected. The only obvious source for the iridium would be the massive pall of dust thrown up by the impact explosion. When the dust finally settled, it would blanket the globe and be preserved in the soil. Since meteoric material is believed to have originated with comets, and possibly asteroids, the iridium-rich layer pointed persuasively at a celestial collision 65 million years ago.

The Berkeley team announced their findings as evidence that an asteroid had impacted the Earth 65 million years ago, causing the extinction holocaust. Other scientists have revised the scenario slightly, making the agent of destruction a comet. (The difference is not crucial, since there is growing evidence that asteroids near the Earth are "dead" comets, as we shall see later.)

Why wasn't all life eradicated by the catastrophe? Ecologist Pierre Beland of Marine Ecosystems, a research company based in Quebec, Canada, offers this explanation: "Once a planet has caught the disease called life, it is hard to wipe out. Any catastrophe is followed by rapid diversification of the remaining species. The effect of the dust cover blocking almost all the sunlight would have been the most severe problem. It couldn't have lasted more than eight months, or virtually everything would have been killed off."

By all standards, the disaster of 65 million years ago was an event of unprecedented proportions. According to Dale Russell, no land animals weighing over 50

1   *Halley's Comet on May 8, 1910.*

2 *Halley's Comet seen on May 12, 1910, on its last approach near the Earth and sun. The comet is expected to be less that one-tenth as bright in 1986.*

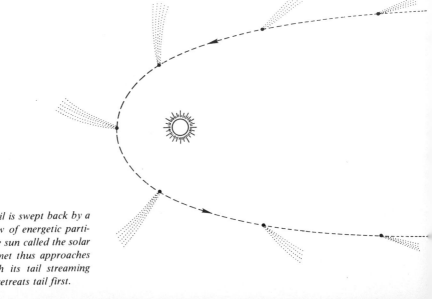

3 *A comet's tail is swept back by a constant flow of energetic particles from the sun called the solar wind. A comet thus approaches the sun with its tail streaming behind and retreats tail first.*

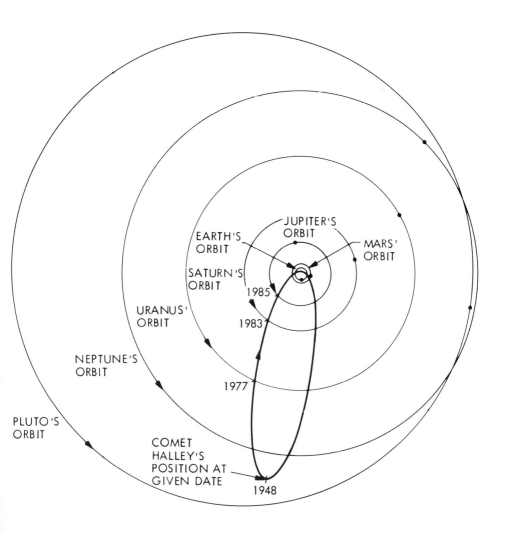

JUPITER'S
ORBIT

EARTH'S
ORBIT

MARS'
ORBIT

SATURN'S
ORBIT

1985

URANUS'
ORBIT

1983

NEPTUNE'S
ORBIT

1977

PLUTO'S
ORBIT

COMET
HALLEY'S
POSITION AT
GIVEN DATE

1948

4

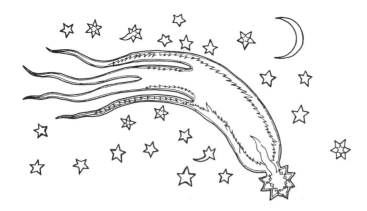

5 *Contemporary drawing of the comet of 1577.*

6 *Fourteen views of Halley's Comet made between April 26*
and June 11, 1910.

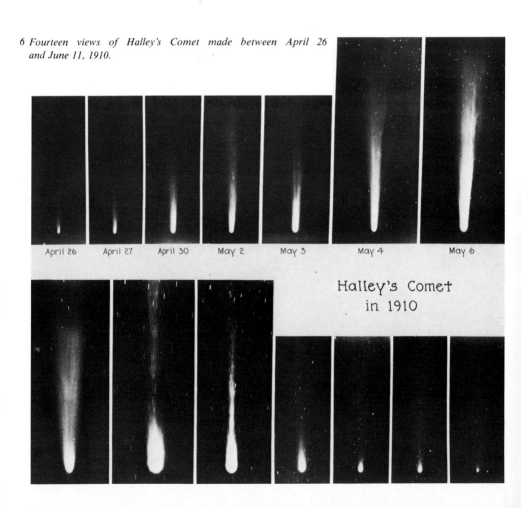

April 26   April 27   April 30   May 2   May 3   May 4   May 6

Halley's Comet
in 1910

Orbit of Halley's Comet

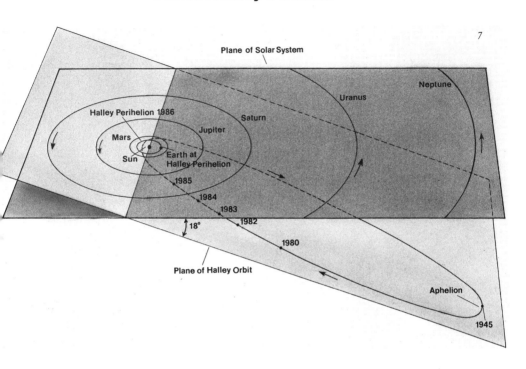

Commemorating the historic events of 1066, the Bayeux Tapestry includes Halley's Comet seen in the spring of that year. At right, King Harold II of England is being informed that the comet is a bad omen, foreshadowing his defeat.

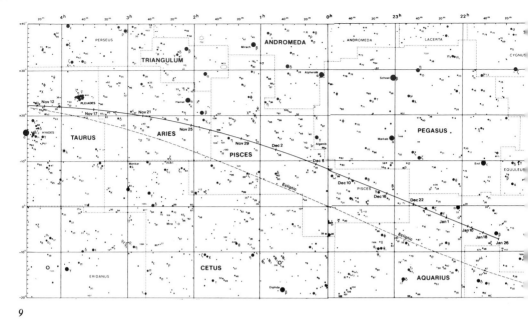

9

Path of Halley's Comet from early November 1985 to late January 1986 when it is conveniently positioned in the evening sky. The comet is expected to brighten from eighth to fourth magnitude during this interval.

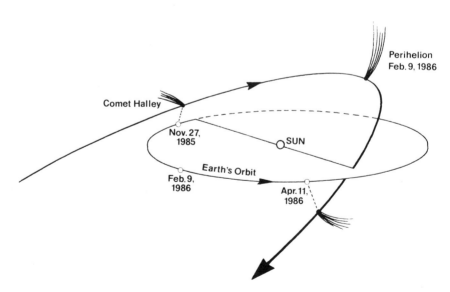

10

During Halley's closest approach to the sun in the winter of 1985—86, the comet will be nearest the Earth on April 11, 1986, at a distance of 39 million miles. On previous trips the comet has swung much closer to us.

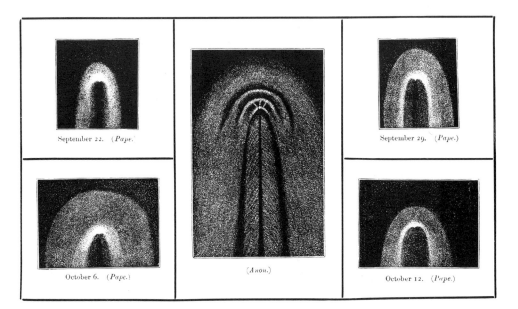

September 22. (*Pape.*)

September 29. (*Pape.*)

October 6. (*Pape.*)

(*Anon.*)

October 12. (*Pape.*)

1 *Before photography became a widely used research tool for comet study, astronomers sat at the telescope eyepiece and drew what they saw, sometimes revealing amazing structure in the comet's coma, They clearly recorded vapors from the comet's nucleus spewing forth, then sweeping back into the tail to form plumes and arcs. Such detail can be detected visually but in bright comets is usually totally obscured in photographs. These illustrations show Donati's Comet of 1858.*

12 *This is one of only a handful of drawings showing the naked-eye appearance of Halley's Comet in 1910.*

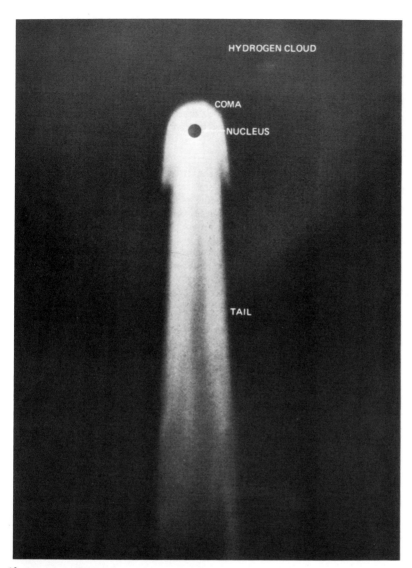

HYDROGEN CLOUD

COMA

NUCLEUS

TAIL

13

Comets have four basic components when they are within a few hundred million miles of the sun. The Coma is the region of dense dust-and-gas emissions boiled from the nucleus by solar radiation. The solar wind sweeps the gas and dust into the visible tail. An invisible hydrogen cloud a million miles or more in diameter, but detected only by spacecraft, surrounds the coma. The black dot indicating the nucleus in this NASA rendering is an exaggeration. Telescopically, the nucleus appears as a point source, and in reality, the icy sphere that constitutes the true nucleus is likely less than 10 miles in diameter.

14 On March 18, 1910, just before the Earth passed through the tail of Halley's Comet, astronomer E. E.
Barnard made this drawing. The comet's coma is below the horizon to the lower left. Within hours the
Earth swept through the tail with no noticeable effect.

15 Dust and debris scattered along the orbit of Halley's Comet produce meteor showers in May and October
each year when the Earth passes near the intersection points.

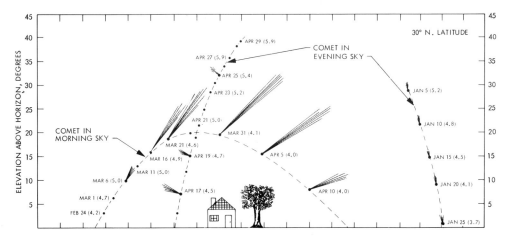

16   *Observing conditions in 1986 for Halley's Comet watchers located about 30 degrees north latitude. Comet positions are for either the beginning of morning twilight or the end of evening twilight. The comet's expected overall magnitude is given in parentheses. Viewing with binoculars and ideal observing conditions are assumed.*

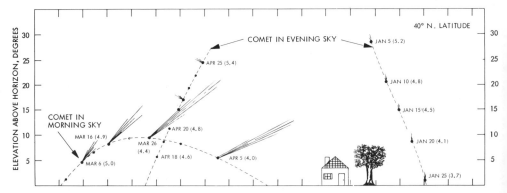

17   *Observing conditions in 1986 for Halley's Comet watchers located about 40 degrees north latitude. Comet positions are for either the beginning of morning twilight or the end of evening twilight. The comet's expected overall magnitude is given in parentheses. Viewing with binoculars and ideal observing conditions are assumed.*

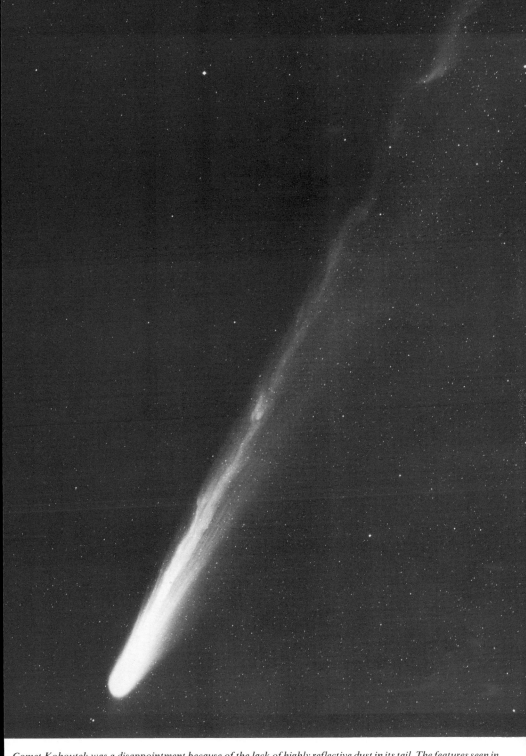

Comet Kohoutek was a disappointment because of the lack of highly reflective dust in its tail. The features seen in the tail in this photo were gases largely invisible to the unaided eye.

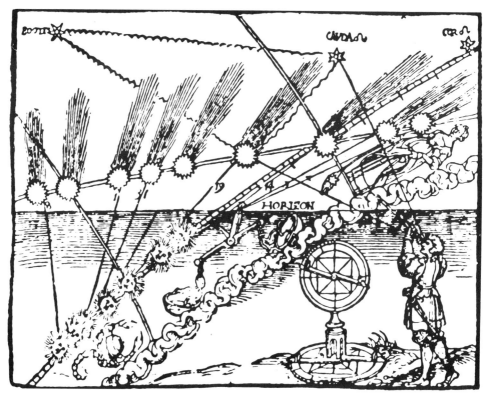

19 Woodcut showing observations of Halley's Comet in August 1531.

20

A telescope in the public park always attracts a crowd, especially when a comet is visible. Here, Parisians are watching comet Coggia of 1874.

21 *Most comets are unspectacular telescopic objects, with feeble tails and comas appearing as unremarkable fuzzy blobs. This is Comet Kobayashi-Berger-Milon seen in August 1975.*

22   *A cartoonist slightly exaggerates the excitement surrounding the discovery of a comet at Greenwich Observatory, England.*

23

Donati's Comet of 1858 brandished a bright scepter-shaped tail with a fainter veil clinging to it.

Like a silver spear, the great comet of 1843 sliced the sky to the delight of millions of onlookers.

25 *A drawing of the Comet of 1882 gives the impression that this object must have been awesome.*

26 *The great comet of 1843, which sported a 100-million-mile-long tail, was one of the most spectacular of all time. The comet's coma is below the horizon in this view from England on March 17, 1843.*

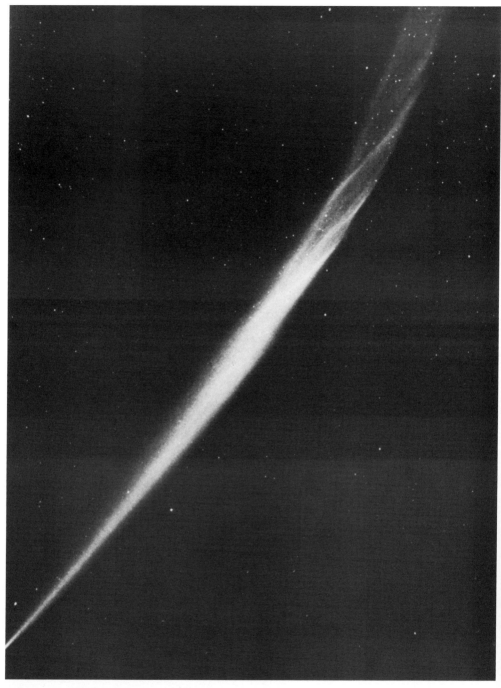

27 *The spectacular comet Ikeya-Seki, the sun-grazer of 1965.*

28 *Seen over Paris in this rendering, Donati's Comet must have been one of the most beautiful comets ever. For about a month its brilliant main dust tail arched across the sky against a backdrop of secondary tails.*

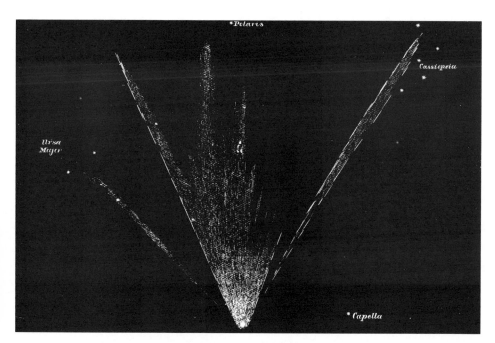

The impressive tail of the comet of 1861 was due largely to its nearness to the Earth. It is seen here fanning out due to perspective. The Earth passed through the tail the next day.

Comet Kohoutek's expected appearance is shown below, based on astronomers' predictions several months before its appearance in the evening sky of January 1974. The bright objects near the comet are Venus and Jupiter. Photo at left shows what was actually seen.

MARCH 8

MARCH 12

MARCH 18

MARCH 23

MARCH 29

APRIL 10

APRIL 24

MAY 24

32

Drawings by comet observer John Bortle chronicle the breakup of the nucleus of Comet West in 1976 into four distinct components, three of which remained as comets in their own right. The breakup released vast quantities of dust, which led to a brilliant fanned tail in the morning sky of March 1976.

COMET MRKOS

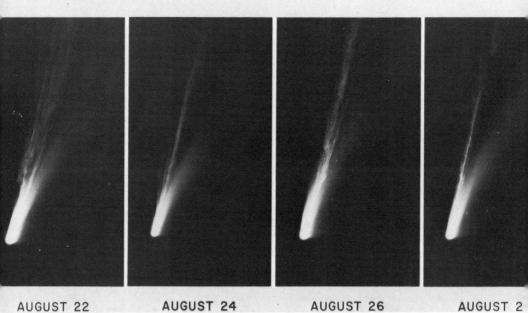

AUGUST 22   AUGUST 24   AUGUST 26   AUGUST 2

33 *The apearance of Comet Mrkos of 1957 is chronicled in these four views. The comet's gas tail appears as a wispy, knotted trail of smoke streaming away from the comet's nucleus. The dust tail is curved and generally featureless. The gas tails of comets appear much fainter than this to the unaided eye.*

34

Comet West of 1976 offered one of the finest displays of any comet in the 20th century.

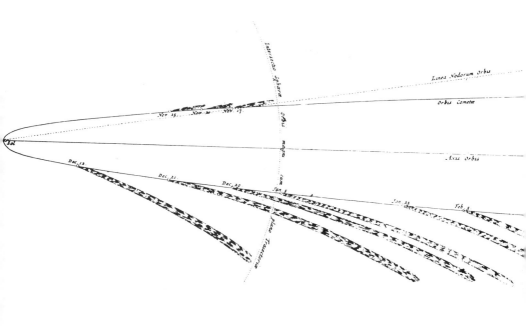

35

One of the great triumphs of 17th-century science was the development of mathematical theories that could explain the orbital maneuverings of comets. This diagram by Edmund Halley, showing the orbit for a comet that appeared in 1680, was published in Newton's Principia, his great treatise on gravity.

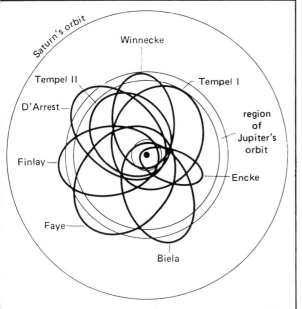

36

The solar system's most massive planet, Jupiter, has "captured" more than 50 comets, including Encke, the comet with the shortest-known period.

37   *Pluto, seen in this artist's rendering from its moon Charon, is known to have a composition similar to that suspect
for comets, leading some atronomers to speculate that both Pluto and Charon are more closely related to come
than the planets of the solar system.

On August 31, 1979, a comet collied with the un, as shown in this sequence of photos btained by a military satellite stationed in Earth orbit as a sentry for nuclear missiles.

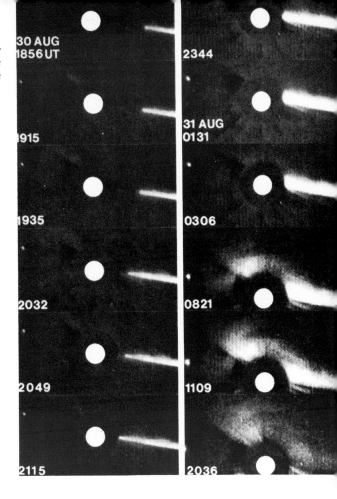

30 AUG
1856 UT

1915

1935

2032

2049

2115

2344

31 AUG
0131

0306

0821

1109

2036

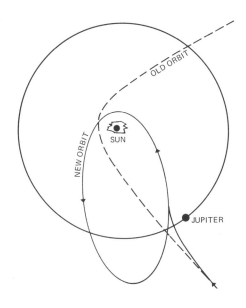

OLD ORBIT

NEW ORBIT

SUN

JUPITER

39 A comet can be gravitationally wrench-
ed from its initial long-period orbit into
a relatively small orbit by a close pass
near Jupiter or one of the other giant
planets. At least 120 comets have been
"captured" by similar gravitational
billiards.

40 Comet Encke has the shortest-known orbital period, 3.3 years. Although it may once have been a conspicuous object, it is now only visible telescopically. The streaks in the photo are stars that produced trails as the telescope follwed the comet's motion during the exposure.

JOHANNIS HEVELII
COMETOGRAPHIA.

41

Seventeenth-century astronomers debating their versio of the orbital motion of comets. A few decades later t problem would be solved by Halley and Newton.

Soviet Venus–Halley Mission

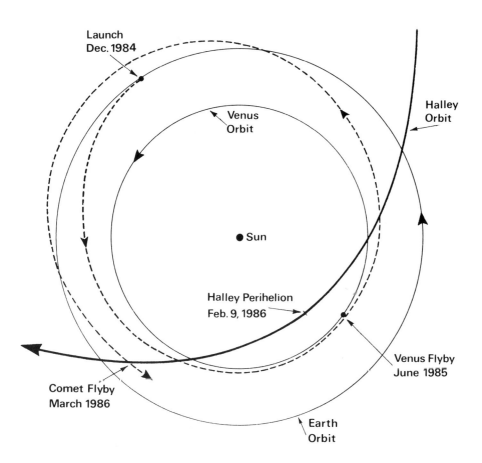

Launch
Dec. 1984

Halley
Orbit

Venus
Orbit

● Sun

Halley Perihelion
Feb. 9, 1986

Venus Flyby
June 1985

Comet Flyby
March 1986

Earth
Orbit

Soviet Union is mounting a major exploration of both Venus and Halley's Comet. Two spacecraft were launched on trajectory shown here in December 1984.

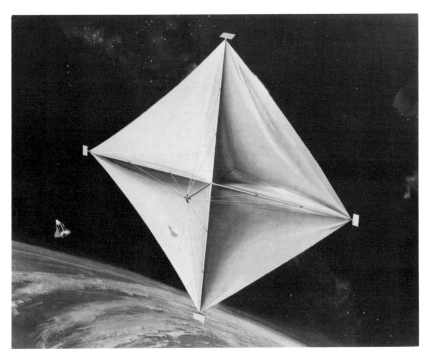

43 *One idea (now discarded) for exploring Halley's Comet was to use a giant sail that would be propelled in the near vacuum of space merely by the pressure of radiation from the sun. Relieved of the burden of carrying its own fuel supply, the solar sail could roam through the solar system indefinitely.*

44

Prior to a series of severe budget cuts, NASA developed plans for a comet rendezvous that included dropping a probe as close to the nucleus as possible.

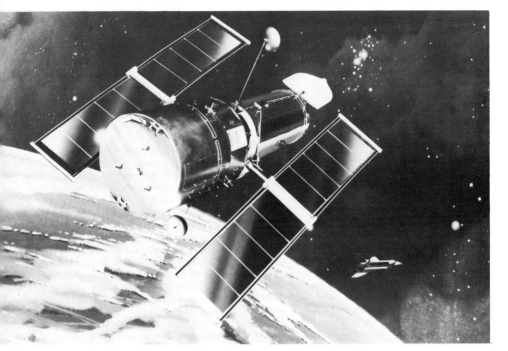

The Space Telescope will be launched from the space shuttle in 1986 just in time to watch the retreat of Halley's Comet. The 94-inch instrument, flying hundreds of miles above the distorting effects of the Earth's atmosphere, will be far powerful than any telescope on Earth.

5

The European Giotto spacecraft hurtles toward the nucleus of Halley's Comet on a kamikaze mission to probe the secrets of Halley's Comet.

47 *An object about the size of a house clobbered northern Arizona about 25,000 years ago creating this mile-wide crater, which has been preserved by the arid climate. Of the countless impact scars elsewhere on Earth that have accumulated over the eons, all but a few hundred have been erased by mountain building, erosion and glaciation.*

48

Forests in central Siberia were leveled for hundreds of square miles in 1908 when a small comet, perhaps a fragment from Comet Encke, collided with the Earth and exploded in the atmosphere before reaching the surface.

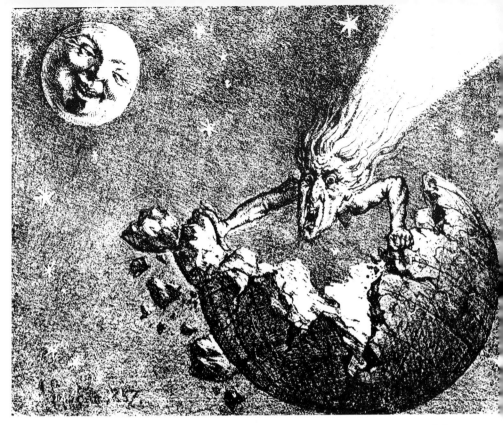

49 *What would happen if a comet collided with the Earth? The disastrous consequences are somewhat exaggerated by a 19th-century French cartoonist.*

50
Concern over the possibility of a comet colliding with the Earth is nothing new. This illustration is from the cover of a pamphlet published in Britain in 1857.

51

Brilliant newly born suns illuminate a section of a vast cloud of dust and gas to produce the magnificent Orion Nebula, faintly visible to the unaided eye in the sword of the constellation Orion.

52   *Thousands of giant clouds of dust and gas in the Milky Way Galaxy are the birthplaces of the stars.*

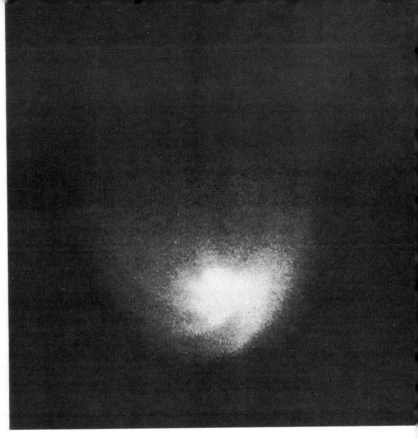

53   *Details of the coma of Comet Bennett, visible during the spring of 1970, reveal strong evidence that the nucleus is spinning, releasing gas and dust in a pinwheel fashion. This phenomenon has been observed in many comets, indicating rotation periods of a few hours.*

54   *The great sun-grazing comet of 1882 was another of the many spectacular comets of the 19th century.*

55 *Comet Bennett provided a dazzling display for early-morning observers in the spring of 1970.*

pounds survived. Nothing even half as devastating is seen anywhere else in the fossil record, and there seems little doubt that the giant comet impact (or whatever it was) 65 million years ago was the greatest disaster in the last 500 million years.

Could it happen again? There seems no way of escaping. It is just a matter of time before the cosmic roulette wheel flings another comet or asteroid our way.

According to the cratering record on the Earth and the moon, nothing more than 10 miles in diameter has collided with either object since life moved onto the land 500 million years ago. Bodies that large seem to be extremely rare in Earth's vicinity, but over three dozen asteroids and an equal number of comets, all one to two miles wide, are known to swing within a few million miles of Earth.

The comets are relatively conspicuous, but asteroids are unobtrusive dark chunks, invisible until they cruise nearby. Earth-approaching asteroids are known as A-pollo objects, after the first discovered. Most have looping paths that carry them from inside Earth's orbit to well beyond Mars, usually deep into the main asteroid belt between Mars and Jupiter. Another group, called Amor objects, cruise well inside Mars' orbit but don't quite make it in to our distance from the sun. A few Apollo asteroids have orbits entirely within that of the Earth. In addition, there are about 50 known Mars-crossing asteroids that never come within 30 million miles of Earth. These are classed simply as Mars-crossers.

"Over long periods of time most Amor asteroids probably evolve into full-time Earth-crossers as a result of strong gravitational perturbations with Mars and the Earth," explains Caltech planetary scientist Eugene Shoemaker. Extrapolating from the number of asteroids seen so far, Shoemaker estimates that there are about 800

Apollos, 500 Amors and 5000 to 10,000 Mars-crossers out there. His research shows that the number of craters six miles in diameter and larger on the 3.3-billion-year-old flat "seas" of the moon's surface and the number of large impact structures found on the ancient shield of North America "are consistent with these estimates."

And yet these fairly secure statistics raise a thorny problem. If Mars-crossers, Amors and Apollos are renegades from the main asteroid belt between Mars and Jupiter, where there is a storehouse of millions of asteroids, one would expect the population to drop off at greater distances from the belt. There are a tenth as many Amors as Mars-crossers, and statistically, there should be a tenth as many Apollos as Amors, since Apollo asteroids are nearest the sun and farthest from the main belt. Instead, there are more Apollos than Amors.

Shoemaker estimates the typical lifetime of an Apollo asteroid is from 20 million to 50 million years, the end coming when it smashes into a planet or has a near miss and is gravitationally ejected from the solar system. "There are far too many Earth-crossing asteroids for them to be coming from the asteroid belt alone," Shoemaker emphasizes. "The attrition rate from collisions and ejections should have weeded most of them out long ago."

Where, then, are the Apollo asteroids coming from? This is where comets return to the picture. We know that periodic comets have been trapped into smaller orbits by a close pass by a planet—usually Jupiter. Such comets quickly get locked into orbits similar to Earth-crossing asteroids. After a few thousand loops around the sun, solar heating would cook the volatile substances in the comet until nothing was left to produce a tail.

An asteroid discovered by Shoemaker's colleague Eleanor Helin in 1979 orbits the sun every 4.5 years, passing from just within the orbit of Earth to near the orbit of Jupiter—just the orbit expected for a comet "captured" during a close approach to Jupiter. According to more recent studies, the object is dull gray and a few miles in diameter, again the expected appearance of a comet corpse. To add to the evidence, Comet Encke loops around the sun in a similar orbit.

Encke is probably well on its way to transforming itself into an Apollo asteroid, according to Zdenek Sekanina of the Jet Propulsion Laboratory. Sekanina believes that Encke, which orbits the sun in 3.3 years, will become extinct in as little as 65 years. Already it shows only a feeble tail as it rounds the point in its orbit nearest the sun. Its ices largely depleted on previous sweeps around the sun, Encke is a weak excuse for a comet. Statistically, gravitational billiards among planets and comets should lock a comet into an Encke-type orbit every 65,000 years or so. That means we probably shouldn't expect to see more than one such active comet, but plenty of dead ones ought to be still around.

Depending on who does the calculations, comet corpses may account for most, or only a fraction, of the Apollo-asteroid population. Everyone agrees that at least a few Apollos come from the main asteroid belt. An asteroid swimming along with its companions in the main belt can only be deflected into an Earth-crossing orbit by a collision, which causes a change in its orbital energy. That, combined with gravitational perturbations from the planets (mainly Jupiter), can swing the body into the inner solar system. Authorities vary on how effective this mechanism is. Shoemaker says it is not efficient enough to supply even half the Apollos we see, but other researchers disagree.

Regardless of their origin, considering the potential threat, it is a little surprising that not one observatory telescope is dedicated entirely to asteroid scouting. In

1981 a NASA scientific advisory panel recommended "Project Spacewatch," a monitoring program with at least one ground-based telescope, ground-based radar and a satellite observation post. "A dedicated Schmidt photographic telescope could detect from 400 to 700 asteroids larger than one kilometer (0.6 mile) in diameter in 20 years of observing," the panel's report states. The scientists went on to propose a 60-inch telescope be built with modern integrated electronics, which would be capable of discriminating asteroids larger than the size of a barn when they come within three million miles (10 times the moon's distance).

Now comes the controversial part of the report: "If a collision with a comet or asteroid were imminent, the orbital modification required would be calculated and a mission deployed to give the object the proper nudge. Once perturbed, the troublemaker would again recede into the Earth-crossing-population background for many thousands of years."

Translation: A missile with a nuclear warhead.

"A nuclear device has a number of attractive features," says NASA scientist Bevan French. "You don't have to actually fix it to the object's surface; you can explode it either on the surface or fairly close to it. This is easy to do technically, since it doesn't matter which direction you shove the asteroid as long as you shove it enough to make it miss the Earth."

Nuclear devices have some problems of course, the biggest being the treaties banning the use of nuclear weapons in space. Such agreements would prohibit conducting the necessary dry runs on comets and asteroids not on collision trajectories. And there is an insidious moral dilemma: Who will assume the awesome responsibility of tampering with the destiny of mankind? The best intentions could backfire. An attempt to divert an on-rushing celestial rogue might alter the trajectory away from its natural course, but not enough to miss the Earth, or might fragment the body into the celestial equivalent of a multiple warhead.

Coupled with these uncertainties is the lack of warning we would have if an asteroid were on a collision course. A half-mile-wide asteroid capable of annihilating most life over a large segment of the United States would probably escape notice until just a week before impact. An object one-tenth that size would likely come in unnoticed by present telescopes until only hours before plunging to the ground. A collision with a comet would herald itself sooner, but there seems little that could be done other than a risky, untried missile attack.

The Siberian impact event erased all doubts about the real potential for a literally Earth-shaking catastrophe. Yet the problem remains at such a low priority that we still don't have one telescope seeking the renegades. Someday the cosmic roulette wheel will pitch a lethal intruder from the abyss our way. The only uncertainty is when.

8
Comets and Life

Humans harbor a deep curiosity about their origins. We want to know how our ancestors evolved from apelike creatures that roamed the African plains five million years ago. The fossil record tells us that living things have inhabited the land for 500 million years, and the sea swarmed with primitive organisms for at least three billion years before that. Going back further, the Earth and the rest of the solar system appear to be about four and a half billion years old. What do comets have to do with any of this? Possibly plenty.

The continuing flow of discoveries in a variety of scientific fields, ranging from microbiology to astrophysics, is constantly clarifying our concepts of the solar system's formation and the subsequent development of life on Earth. In recent years strong evidence has been gathered suggesting that comets likely played an overwhelmingly crucial role during this genesis period by providing a favorable environment for the emergence of life. If correct, these theories catapult comets from celestial curiosities to literally the stuff from which humankind is made.

The story of comets and life that embodies these new ideas begins more than four and a half billion years ago when the solar system was born from a collapsing nebula of interstellar gas and dust. These giant nebular clouds, often thousands of light-years in diameter, are littered throughout the spiral arms of the Milky Way Galaxy. You can see them on a dark night; the Milky Way has a tattered appearance due to the obscuring effect of dark nebulas blocking the light from millions of stars behind them. Some nebulas, such as the famous one in Orion's sword, which is visible to the unaided eye as a faint, out-of-focus star, are illuminated by the stars recently born within them.

The mechanism that causes these great gaseous maternity wards to condense into stars is only roughly understood. One widely accepted theory suggests that the shock wave from an exploding star can trigger a compression in a cloud which ultimately leads to the birth of stars. Another theory says the same effect can be achieved as the cloud passes through a density wave in the galaxy's spiral arms. In any case, there is no doubt that stars do form from nebulas since the stars seen embedded in them have all the characteristics of the youngest-known stars.

With the help of computer simulations, astronomers attempting to understand the dynamics of the collapsing cloud that formed our sun and its family of planets observe that the maximum stability in a huge contracting blob of gas and dust is maintained if the material whirls itself into a disk with the highest concentration of matter at the disk's nucleus. This same shape is seen many times in nature, including the overall form of the Milky Way Galaxy.

Using radio and infrared telescopes, researchers have probed the feeble radiation from the nebulas where stars are being born and discovered that they are composed of hydrogen, helium and a multitude of simple molecules, compounds of hydrogen, carbon, oxygen and nitrogen. Abundant among these is water (H_2O), carbon dioxide (CO_2), hydrogen cyanide (HCN) and formaldehyde (CH_2O), all essential building blocks for the molecules of life. Molecules containing up to 13 atoms have been detected in interstellar clouds, and more complex ones are certainly out there.

As a cloud like the one that presumably formed our solar system contracts, the molecules are attracted to the cloud's dust grains, in a manner analogous to the way water droplets initially form as a storm cloud builds. Once the material at the disk-shaped cloud's center becomes dense enough so that pressures exceed a critical value, thermonuclear reactions (hydrogen-bomb-type reactions) are ignited, and the sun begins to flood surrounding space with radiation. During this early stage the primordial sun is thought to have been up to 100 times hotter than it is today. In the inner zone of the disk, inside the present orbit of Jupiter, water and other volatile compounds, such as those listed above, soon evaporate from the tiny dust grains. Outside Jupiter's distance solar radiation is not strong enough to produce much of this evaporation, so most of the molecules from the mother cloud remain intact.

The next stage in solar system formation is the gradual assimilation of the particles of the cloud into planetesimals, small bodies from which the planets are to be made, ranging up to about 50 miles in diameter. The planetesimals inside the orbit of Jupiter—produced from the dust grains from which the water and other volatile light elements were evaporated by solar heating—would be rocky bodies. Those outside Jupiter's orbit, still containing the water and other molecules, would be iceballs—identical to comet nuclei.

The swarms of planetesimals would form a colossal ring system around the sun similar to Saturn's, only on a much larger scale. Trillions of planetesimals whirling in a giant disk around the sun would bump into each other, perhaps breaking apart but often sticking to each other because of the low velocity of collision, since they are all going around the sun in the same direction. Through a gradual accretion process, the planets are born. The inner planets—Mercury, Venus, Earth, Mars and Earth's moon, which is of near planetary dimensions—are all rocky bodies formed from the rocky planetesimals. The asteroid belt appears to be leftover material from this process.

Jupiter, Saturn, Uranus and Neptune are formed from the accretion of the much more abundant comet planetesimals. These worlds contain vast storehouses of hydrogen, helium, carbon, nitrogen and oxygen. Indeed, Uranus and Neptune seem to be almost exactly the composition one would expect if trillions of comets were collected in one spot and compacted into a single body. Because of their enormous bulk and gravitational influence, the most massive planets of the solar system, Jupiter and Saturn, appear to have been able to capture extra amounts of hydrogen and helium available in their orbital zones during the early phases of solar system formation.

This genesis scenario has been worked out in large part from computer simulations of the suspected conditions that existed in the early solar system. That is, astronomers asked what must have happened if you start out with an interstellar cloud and you end up with the solar system. The events just described represent one hypothesis that has recently gained the support of several theorists. This concept also suggests that the inner rocky planets took less than a million years to form, coinciding with the first burst of radiation from the primordial sun. In the outer solar system things happened at a much more leisurely pace. Uranus and Neptune probably were not completely formed for half a billion years or more.

In addition to the cometary planetesimals involved directly in the formation of Uranus and Neptune, there would have been many more that missed being gravitationally pulled into Uranus and Neptune or swept up by them as they orbited the sun. These objects, as we discovered in Chapter 5, were flung on a multitude of different trajectories by the gravitational influences of Uranus and Neptune. Many were pitched into the Oort cloud, others ejected from the solar system entirely and another group flung toward the inner solar system. The quantities of comets around at this time was prodigious. The initial stockpile may have been as great as a million billion.

If we could be transported back to the primordial Earth, say, 300 million years after its formation, the sky would be ablaze with a thousand comets every night. Every few years one of them would collide with the Earth, releasing a vast cargo of water, carbon dioxide and other hydrogen-carbon-nitrogen-oxygen compounds. Some theories of solar system formation indicate that the Earth at this time did not have its own atmosphere. Radiation pressure from the dazzling primal sun and heat generated by the impact of the rocky bodies that continued to pummel the Earth after its initial formation would be great enough to boil off much of whatever primordial atmosphere there was. These theories suggest that the oceans as well as the atmosphere of the Earth came from the comets that were deflected from their orbits in the outer solar system during the slow accretion of Uranus and Neptune. Even a conservative estimate of the number of comets that would have collided with the Earth could easily provide the amount of water now in Earth's oceans and more than a hundred times the quantity of gases needed to form the present atmosphere.

"It makes sense to believe that the early atmosphere of the Earth was indeed this atmosphere brought about by comets and not a hypothetical primordial atmosphere that should have been condensed by some obscure mechanism out of the primordial gas of the protostar nebula," says Armand Delsemme, astrophysicist at the University of Toledo. Delsemme points out that the time scale makes sense: The comets were in Earth's vicinity in large numbers for half a billion years, until about four billion years ago. Soon thereafter, the continents, oceans and early atmoshpere of the Earth stabilized. No rocks on Earth have ever been found that date prior to 3.9 billion years ago.

This scenario thus moves comets into the role of providing the environment on Earth necessary for life that emerged between 3.5 and 3.9 billion years ago. Of course, the Earth had to be at the appropriate distance from the sun to allow the oceans to remain liquid. Venus, the same size as the Earth, was almost certainly supplied with the same abundant cometary material. But because Venus is nearer the sun, the liquid water on its surface has long since vaporized. The planet is now shrouded in a dense carbon-dioxide atmosphere that acts as a greenhouse, producing global surface temperatures of 850° F. In the case of Mars, farther from the sun, the water on its surface has either escaped into space or is frozen underground as permafrost.

As for the key question of how life emerged, there is no definite answer. The molecules that exist in interstellar clouds which may have been carried to Earth inside cometary fragments are, in an evolutionary sense, a long way from the simplest one-celled creatures that apparently populated the Earth's oceans at least three and a half billion years ago. (Evidence of these creatures comes through examination of microfossils embedded in the oldest Earth rocks.)

The problem of the genesis of living matter will likely vex scientists for a few generations yet. In an evolutionary sense, the difference between the precursor molecules presumed to have been carried to Earth by comets and the most primitive one-celled organisms that we know of is something like the difference between a pile of engine parts—levers, valves, shafts, cylinders and so on—and a smoothly running well-tuned engine. Taking all the engine parts and throwing them into a box with some gasoline won't produce the running engine. The mystery is compounded because in the geological time scale it happened almost overnight, in a few hundred million years. Stated another way, the difference between the molecules in interstellar clouds and the simplest one-celled creatures, called anaerobic bacteria, is the same as the difference in complexity between anaerobic bacteria and humans, and yet the latter evolution has required over three billion years.

Renegade theorists, such as Britain's Sir Fred Hoyle, have proposed an even more exotic role for comets in the history of life. Hoyle suggests that inside a comet the natural decay of radioactive elements would melt the interior ices, providing a crucible for the trapped interstellar organic molecules to cook themselves, in a sort of cosmic womb, into ever more complex molecuar chains. In this protected environment, he proposes that one-celled creatures, such as bacteria, were created and subsequently deposited on the Earth. Thus Hoyle shifts the critical genesis link between organic molecules and one-celled organisms from the primordial oceans of Earth to the interiors of comets. Since 1978, when he first proposed it, Hoyle's scenario has remained an extreme minority viewpoint.

The majority of theorists in the field believe that the synthesis of living one-celled organisms occurred on the Earth over three billion years ago, when the planet was covered with water and cloaked in an atmosphere somewhat denser than today's. Exactly how it happened is one of the towering unknowns of science. But there now seems little doubt that comets played a critical role in the chain of events. As we focus more closely on this mystery in the years ahead, it may well become obvious that every living thing, along with the water and air we require for our survival, is nothing more than interstellar frost brought to Earth by comets.

9

Equipment for Viewing and Photographing Halley's Comet

Everybody wants to see Halley's Comet on its once-in-a-lifetime jaunt through our sector of the solar system, and the best way to do it is to be prepared with the right kind of optical equipment and to use that equipment from the best viewing site possible.

Selecting the optimum observation post begins by scouting the countryside within a reasonable driving distance of your home. Choose a moonless night so the darkest location will be obvious. The site should be free from any direct interference from house and street lights while at the same time retaining a generally unobstructed view of the horizon, especially in the southeast and southwest sectors. A high location is preferable but not essential. The most important factor is that it be accessible and as close to pitch-black as possible. This is where you will best see Halley's Comet, and many other celestial wonders as a bonus.

Choosing optical equipment is not nearly as straight-forward as finding a dark site. As the comet nears Earth, telescope manufacturers will step up their ad campaigns, stating that their telescopes will zoom you in for the best view of the great comet. When it comes to observing comets, not all telescopes are created equal. Certain types have inherent advantages over other types. Unfortunately, many telescope owners are going to be disappointed with the view their instruments yield when it comes time to seek out the famous interplanetary wanderer. Avoiding this pitfall requires some background on the various types of telescopes and what they do best. Here's what you need to know.

There are three main types of telescopes on the market today: refractors, reflectors and catadioptric, or compound, instruments. They range in price from less than $100 to $10,000 for instruments that rival those used by professional astronomers. As a general guideline, telescopes priced less than $200 are not suitable for anything but the most introductory pursuits in backyard astronomy, such as viewing the moon, the brightest double stars, and the planets Jupiter and Saturn. In my opinion, these are toys rather than astronomical telescopes and should be regarded as options of last resort. In the case of Halley's Comet, binoculars will probably give a better overall view than many inexpensive scopes, for reasons that will be described in a moment.

The key point to keep in mind is that when Halley's Comet is at its best, in late December 1985 and January and April 1986, it will have a tail several degrees in length, possibly more than five degrees. Five degrees is the distance between the Big Dipper's two front stars, the pair that point to the North Star. That's about the width of three fingers held at arm's length, Boy Scout fashion.

Few telescopes are capable of taking in an object anywhere near that large in a single view, whereas binoculars do it easily. The whole comet will be seen framed in a starry background in binoculars, making them almost mandatory equipment for viewing Halley regardless of what other instruments you may use.

Any pair of binoculars will do, but my choice is the 7x50 or 10x50 models, which have 7 power and 10 power respectively. Their 50mm (2-inch) lenses collect 36 times as much light as the unaided eye, thus producing an image of the comet 36 times brighter. Magnification is definitely secondary to the brightness factor, which is determined by the diameter of the main lens in any optical instrument. Most binoculars have fields of view from 6 to 8 degrees.

Refractor telescopes use lenses, as do binoculars. Most refractors sold in department and camera stores have main objective lenses 60mm in diameter, barely larger than those of binoculars. This is only a 40 percent improvement over 50mm binoculars, from 36 to 50 times the light-gathering power of the eye. Furthermore, most refractors have long focal ratios, that is, the distance to the point where the image comes to focus is 10 to 15 times greater than the diameter of the main lens. For example, a 60mm refractor with a focal point 900mm from the main lens has a focal ratio of $f/15$ (900 divided by 60 = 15).

Long focal ratios translate into narrow fields of view. This is of no consequence when viewing the moon, double stars and planets, tasks for which refractors are ideal. But the small field of view of refractors (usually less than 1½ degrees) combined with modest light-collecting ability makes these instruments poor choices for comet watching. Yet because they are mass-produced and sold at relatively low prices compared with other types of telescopes, small refractors are the most commonly advertised telescope for viewing Halley's Comet. This is strictly advertising hype. Binoculars selling for less than half as much will be easier to use and will provide generally more pleasing views of Halley. (Special short-focal-ratio refractors of 80mm or greater aperture are an exception and do make excellent comet scopes, but these instruments are usually more expensive and not widely available.)

The *reflector telescope* is almost always found in the configuration developed three centuries ago by Isaac Newton, known today, naturally enough, as the Newtonian reflector. Its main optical element is a mirror located at the base of the tube, fashioned with a precise curvature to reflect incoming light to the top of the tube where a smaller flat-surface mirror angled at 45 degrees reflects the light out the side to a focuser and magnifying eyepiece. The smallest Newtonian reflectors have main mirrors three inches (75mm) in diameter, which collect 80 times as much light as the unaided eye, more than twice as much as 50mm binoculars. However, Newtonian reflectors also come in 4-inch and larger sizes at modest prices, whereas refractors larger than 2.4 inches (60mm) are generally quite pricey.

As described above, a large focal ratio is a distinct disadvantage for comet observation. Newtonian reflectors generally have much shorter focal ratios than refractors, usually f/10 or less. One instrument, the Edmund Astroscan, is a 4 1/8-inch (105mm) f/4 Newtonian reflector. This telescope collects 150 times the light of the human eye, producing bright, crisp images in addition to having the largest field of view—three degrees—of any widely available commercial telescope. This is the ideal combination for comet viewing. In addition, the Astroscan has, as a by-product of its unique lightbulb-shaped housing, a built-in universal ball-and-socket-type mount that requires only a small table-top stand to keep it perfectly steady for celestial observation. The telescope can be placed on a car hood, treestump, picnic bench— anything that will provide a convenient platform. Furthermore, the instrument has an over-the-shoulder strap that turns it into a totally portable instrument for stable hand-held viewing. The instument's portability, wide field of view, high light-collecting ability and ease of use make it the ideal Halley's Comet telescope.

Larger Newtonian reflectors will, because of their greater light-collecting ability, produce even brighter images of the comet, but their more restricted fields of view mean that when the comet is at its best, the entire object may not be seen in a single view. Nonetheless, all things considered, Newtonian reflectors of any aperture are probably superior to the other types for comet viewing.

Compound telescopes combine many of the better attributes of refractors and Newtonian reflectors. They come in two versions: Schmidt-Cassegrain and Maksutov-Cassegrain. In recent years, Schmidt-Cassegrains have become the most popular of the two. Both types have a mirror at the base of the tube, as in a Newtonian reflector, which concentrates the light onto a smaller mirror at the top of the tube. But instead of directing the light off at an angle out the side of the tube, as in the Newtonian, the smaller secondary mirror sends the light back through a hole in the main mirror and out the rear of the telescope, where the focuser is located. A lens at the front of the tube supports the secondary mirror.

Schmidt-Cassegrains and Maksutov-Cassegrains come in all sizes from a 3½-inch aperture to a 14-inch. In their smallest sizes, these instruments are priced in the $400 to $700 range; however, at 3½-inch aperture, they do not equal, for example, the 4 1/8-inch aperture of the Astroscan. Furthermore, their focal ratios, usually f/10, do not permit the wide field of view of shorter Newtonian designs. Focal-reducing accessories are available for larger Schmidt-Cassegrains, but these instruments are for the serious backyard astronomer and are generally priced in the $1000 to $2000 range.

Schmidt-Cassegrains are widely used in amateur astronomy because of their versatility and ability to show many different types of celestial objects well. However, they are not ideal scopes for comet watching. All things considered, a short-focal-ratio Newtonian reflector in the 4-to-6-inch range, such as the Edmund Astroscan, is the ideal Halley's Comet telescope. Such an instrument also will have many other uses in the years to come because the features that make it suitable for comet watching also make it ideal for hunting down asteroids, galaxies and star clusters and for scanning the Milky Way.

I've left the subject of magnification until now because it is probably the most misunderstood aspect of amateur telescopes. It is only natural for the neophyte to assume that a 60mm refractor telescope that is capable of magnifications as high as 400x will reveal celestial objects in immensely more detail than, say, 7 power binoculars. Yet as mentioned earlier, this same refractor with a 60mm aperture has only 40 percent more light-collecting power than the binoculars. Although these telescopes can theoretically magnify 400 times, astronomers call such amplification empty magnification. It is also false advertising.

According to the physics of the interaction of optics and light, a telescope cannot reveal any additional detail once magnification has reached 2 power for each millimeter of aperture. Thus a 60mm refractor's maximum useful magnification is 120x. And even though such magnifications are possible, they are seldom used in practice. In fact, for comet watching, the reverse is the case. The most impressive views of Halley's Comet will be at the *lowest* magnification available on a particular telescope. Here again, the refractors and compound telescopes are at a disadvantage. They are usually supplied with low-power eyepieces that yield about 35 power. This limit is due to long focal ratios. Short-focal-ratio telescopes such as the Edmund Astroscan can be used at powers as low as 16x.

Similarly, binoculars are also designed to use the lowest practical magnification for their particular optical systems. Low magnification is used for comet viewing for two reasons. One, it provides the widest field of view, which permits seeing as much of the comet at one time as possible. Two, low magnification produces the brightest images. The higher the magnification, the more the light is spread out and hence the dimmer the image becomes. Thus both the brightest images and the widest field of view are obtained at the lowest magnification.

The bottom line is that a combination of large aperture and low magnification produces the best comet scopes. But there is a practical limit to a telescope's aperture. Not only are larger-aperture telescopes more expensive (although Newtonian reflectors are least so), they are also much more cumbersome to transport to a dark site than their smaller cousins. Since travelling away from light-polluted urban environs to a rural location is mandatory for a decent look at Halley, a modest-sized telescope is recommended for convenience if nothing else. On all these counts, a telescope like the Edmund Astroscan is clearly the ideal choice.

Photographing the Comet

The bad news is that unless you have experience in astrophotography, you likely will not be successful in photographing Halley's Comet through your telescope. Although it is possible, it is a difficult procedure best left to those who have taken dozens of through-the-telescope portraits of other celestial objects. However, the good news is that surprisingly bright and realistic pictures of the comet can be obtained with a standard single-lens-reflex camera loaded with a roll of the excellent high-speed color films now available (400 speed or higher).

A 10-second to 2-minute exposure using the standard 50mm or 55mm lens will easily reveal the comet when it is at its brightest. A camera tripod and bulb shutter release will be necessary to keep the camera steady during the exposure. If the exposure is more than about 15 seconds, the stars will appear as small streaks instead of dots, due to Earth's rotation. The images of both stars and comet will be seriously distorted in pictures over two minutes unless the camera can be attached to the tube of an equatorially mounted telescope that tracks the stars.

Experiment with various exposures so that you will end up with at least one photo that is realistic and esthetically pleasing. Best results are usually obtained with the lens adjusted to its lowest focal ratio, which allows the largest amount of light to reach the film. The camera, of course, should be focused at infinity. Foreground objects such as trees or distant buildings usually add interest to the composition. A good color photograph of Halley's Comet will be a prize for a lifetime, and surprisingly good results can be achieved with modest equipment.

YOUR RECORD OF HALLEY'S COMET

Date of Observation	Time From—To	Overall Magnitude (estimate)	Length of Tail (estimate)	Moon in Sky?	Remarks

RECOMMENDED READING

There are relatively few comprehensive, but readable books on comets, compared to those available on other aspects of astronomy. Here are some of the best, which are not overly technical:

Comets, Meteorites and Men by Peter L. Brown, Taplinger, New York (1974). An excellent reference source filled with fascinating historical reports as well as reasonably up-to-date facts and theories.

The Comet Is Coming by Nigel Calder, Viking Press, New York (1980). A witty and somewhat irreverent look at the great comet and comets in general by one of the world's top science writers.

Edmund Halley: Genius in Eclipse by Colin A. Ronan, Doubleday, New York (1969). A comprehensive and readable biography of one of the great scientists of all time.

The following four books are suggested for anyone interested in backyard skywatching, with or without a telescope:

The Edmund Sky Guide by Terence Dickinson and Sam Brown, Edmund Scientific, Barrington, N.J. (1978). An ultrasimplified introduction to the sky; an ideal first book for beginning stargazers.

The Edmund Mag 6 Star Atlas by Terence Dickinson, Victor Costanzo and Glenn F. Chaple, Edmund Scientific, Barrington, N.J. (1982). In conjunction with the above, this book provides almost everything you need to know about using a telescope and finding your way around the night sky.

The Observer's Handbook (published annually by The Royal Astronomical Society of Canada, 124 Merton St., Toronto M4S 2Z2). Indispensable guide for skywatchers. Contains a wide selection of amazingly detailed tables on everything from impact craters on Earth to a list of the brightest galaxies and quasars.

The Astronomical Calendar by Guy Ottewell (published annually by the Dept. of Physics, Furman University, Greenville, SC 29613). This large-format guidebook gives positions of the planets for the whole year, details of meteor showers, finder charts for comets and asteroids and much more. Highly recommended. Little direct overlap with The Observer's Handbook.

There are many general books on astronomy. One of the best is:

Astronomy: The Cosmic Journey by William K. Hartmann, Wadsworth, Menlo Park, Calif. (1982). Hartmann describes every facet of the subject in detail except practical backyard aspects covered by the four books above.

ABOUT THE AUTHOR

Terence Dickinson is a science journalist specializing in astronomy. He has held scientific staff positions at the Strasenburgh Planetarium in Rochester, N.Y., the Royal Ontario Museum and the Ontario Science Centre and was editor of Astronomy magazine from 1973 to 1975. Since 1976 he has devoted full time to writing. This is his third book for Edmund Scientific.

ILLUSTRATION CREDITS

1. Hale Observatories
2. Hale Observatories
3. Victor Costanzo
4. Donald Yeomans
5. NASA
6. Hale Observatories
7. Victor Costanzo
8. Bayeux Trustees
9. Victor Costanzo
10. Victor Costanzo
11. Pape from Chambers
12. Splendor of the Heavens
13. NASA
14. E.E. Barnard
15. Victor Costanzo
16. Donald Yeomans
17. Donald Yeomans
18. Hale Observatories
19. NASA
20. Chambers
21. Jack Newton

22.   Chambers

23.   Chambers

24.   Chambers

25.   American Museum

26.   Chambers

27.   Kitt Peak National Observatory

28.   NASA

29.   Chambers

30.   Arnold Richards

31.   Victor Costanzo

32.   John Bortle

33.   Hale Observatories

34.   Marvin Mayo

35.   Royal Astronomical Society

36.   Paolo Maffei

37.   Ray Crane

38.   U.S. Naval Observatory

39.   NASA

40.   U.S. Naval Observatory

41.   Royal Astronomical Society

42.   Victor Costanzo

43.   NASA

44.   Brian Sullivan

45.   NASA

46.   Brian Sullivan

47.   World Wide

48.   Novosti Press

49.   NASA

50.   Peter Lancaster Brown

51.   Joe Cocozza

52.   Bart Bok

53.   Lunar & Planetary Laboratory

54.   Chambers

55.   James Brady